Saint Katharine Drexel

Saint Katharine Drexel

Friend of the Oppressed

by Ellen Tarry

Pauline
BOOKS & MEDIA
Boston

Library of Congress Cataloging-in-Publication Data

Tarry, Ellen, 1906–
    Saint Katharine Drexel, friend of the oppressed / by Ellen
Tarry.—Rev. and updated ed.
            p. cm.
Rev. ed of: Katharine Drexel, friend of the neglected.
    ISBN 0-8198-7042-0 (pbk.)
    1. Drexel, Katharine Mary, 1858-1955. I. Tarry, Ellen 1906–
Katharine Drexel, friend of the neglected. II. Title.
    BX4705.D755 .T3 2000
    27'.97—dc21

                                                                        00-010176

Originally published under the title *Katharine Drexel: Friend of the Neglected,* by Farrar, Straus & Cudahy, Inc. Later reprinted as *Katharine Drexel: Friend of the Oppressed* by Winston-Derek Publishers, Inc.

All photographs, unless otherwise noted, courtesy of the Sisters of the Blessed Sacrament Archives.

Photographs of Amy Wall courtesy of Joanna Lightner.

Prayers and Contemplative Reflections from the Personal Writings of Saint Katharine Drexel reprinted from *Praying with Mother Katharine Drexel,* with the kind permission of the Sisters of the Blessed Sacrament.

Revised and updated edition

Copyright © 2000, by Ellen Tarry

Printed and published in the U.S.A. by Pauline Books & Media, 50 Saint Pauls Avenue, Boston MA 02130-3491.

www.pauline.org

Pauline Books & Media is the publishing house of the Daughters of St. Paul, an international congregation of women religious serving the Church with the communications media.

2 3 4 5 6 7 8   06 05 04 03 02 01

Contents

FOREWORD

Ellen Tarry writes gently. Perhaps that's why her little book brought me close to tears. Or perhaps it's because I became a child again as I read, the child I was in Philadelphia when my father first told me of Mother Katharine Drexel. I have read much of Mother Katharine through the years, but nothing has transported me back to those days when she first became my heroine, except for this little gem of Ellen Tarry's.

It was good to be in Rome, as I was, on that twentieth day of November 1988 when Pope John Paul II declared Mother Katharine to be "Blessed." It was even better to be in Saint Charles Borromeo School in Harlem, on February 15, 1990, to see, talk, and listen to the hundreds of Black youngsters there being taught and formed in the love of Jesus and his Church by the Sisters of the Blessed Sacrament, founded by Mother Katharine. Those sisters are nothing short of marvelous; the youngsters placed in their hands are among the luckiest in the world.

Never in my growing-up days did I dream that I would one day be president of an organization for the Black and Native American Missions which raises and distributes millions of dollars for the very same kind of charities Mother Katharine initiated so many years ago. Even this organization's headquarters reminds us of Mother Katharine. It's a lovely old house in

Washington, once her own home, now the organization's as her gift. I have always felt her presence when I enter there. I think of her courage, am awed by her spirit of poverty, thrilled by her holiness.

Ellen Tarry's own love for Mother Katharine breathes through every page of her text. It is my hope and prayer that every person who has the privilege of reading this book will also come to know and love her, this saint for our times.

John Cardinal O'Connor
Archbishop of New York
April 6, 2000

PREFACE

Few authors have been privileged to write a book about the person who has, in the spiritual sense, been the source of their greatest gift...the gift of faith. In writing about Reverend Mother M. Katharine Drexel, this has been my privilege.

It was through the Sisters of the Blessed Sacrament, founded by Mother Katharine, that I discovered the Eucharistic Lord. I discovered him who waits in the tabernacles throughout the world, for all to come to him so that he may open the door to his Father through the teachings of Holy Mother Church.

The awesome responsibility of such a labor of love might have stilled my pen but for the encouragement and help of Mother Mary Anselm, Mother Mary Pius, who first suggested this book, and Sister Mary Timothy of Saint Elizabeth's Convent, Cornwells Heights, Pennsylvania, Motherhouse of the Sisters of the Blessed Sacrament, who answered my many requests for information.

Had it not been for permission granted to me by Mother Anselm to use as a source of material, *The Francis A. Drexel Family*, edited by the late Sister Mary Dolores, S.B.S., this biography of Mother Katharine could not have been written. If permission had not also been given to me to create dialog, and to enrich certain scenes with details, I would not have felt free to weave a story around the life of one of such sacred memory. All of the major incidents are true. Every character is real.

All of the members of Katharine Drexel's religious family at Saint Elizabeth's Convent have made a generous contribution in giving me access to documents and publications pertaining to the life of their foundress. I am especially grateful to those sisters at Cornwells Heights and at Torresdale who reminisced and explained as we strolled along paths, which once felt the touch of Mother Katharine's feet. They helped me recall much of the story of the early days of this community dedicated to the service of both African and Native Americans. I had heard that story many years before from the lips of the late Sister Mary Inez, one of the original band of thirteen women who accompanied Mother Katharine on the journey from Pittsburgh to open the first novitiate at Torresdale.

A special acknowledgement is made to my friend, George K. Hunton, executive secretary of the New York Catholic Interracial Council, for sharing with me his memories of conversations with Mother Katharine and with her devoted sister, the late Mrs. Edward Morrell, during the years when the Catholic Interracial Council was one of their main interests.

My own spiritual advisor, Monsignor Cornelius J. Drew, lent his assistance in many ways to this small effort. I must also thank close friends and family—my mother and daughter—for bearing with me during the months when I retreated from the demands of everyday life while enjoying the words, actions, prayer, and adventures of Kate Drexel who became Mother Katharine.

It was many years ago, when June was in the meadows and the sun shone bright in the recreation hall at Saint Francis de Sales in Rock Castle, Virginia—just as bright as a July sun is shining on my desk while I write—that Mother Katharine handed me a diploma. Just as that same sun shines today, the same helpful love with which Mother Anselm and Sister Mary Timothy prepared me for that graduation has flown along the course of years to make this book possible. It is therefore a gesture of appreciation to all of the Sisters of the Blessed Sacrament from one of their own children.

July 24, 1957

Many changes have taken place since the first edition of this book was published. Most of the dear teachers who encouraged me to write this story have gone on to their eternal reward. Katharine Drexel, whom we referred to then as Reverend Mother, is being elevated to sainthood. The Sisters of the Blessed Sacrament, which she founded, is now a congregation of religious women of all nationalities, and has already celebrated a centennial of life and work in the Church. Even the town in which the Motherhouse is located has undergone a change. Cornwells Heights is now Bensalem, Pennsylvania, according to the U.S. Postal Service. Yet, the same spirit of love, devotion, and abundant good works is a part of every nook and cranny at Saint Elizabeth Convent in Bensalem. There, where all of us—all who have been nurtured by Mother Katharine Drexel or her daughters in religion—still gather to thank God and celebrate his blessings.

This author is especially grateful to Sister M. Juliana Haynes, former President of the Sisters of the Blessed Sacrament, and Sisters M. Thomasita Daley and Mary Ellen Quilty. However, I must admit it was the late Sister M. Maurice

Enright who, through the years, encouraged me to have the book republished with her: "We must get that book back in print. We need it."

Saint Francis de Sales High School, my beloved *Castle*, was closed at the end of the 1970 school year due to a decline in enrollment. Saint Emma Industrial and Agricultural Institute (Belmead), was closed in 1972 for the same reason. Yet, the Sisters of the Blessed Sacrament together with their Alumni and the Saint Francis/Saint Emma Alumni Association keep alive the memory of both institutions. And through them, the spirit of Mother Katharine Drexel lives on in our land.

July 2000

Chapter 1

An Heiress Grows Up

Katharine blinked tiredly, for sleep comes early to a girl not yet five. It had been some time since her sister had called downstairs to their mother and father, and still they had not come up. The Drexels always said their night prayers together, whether they were at home in Philadelphia, or—as they were tonight—in their cottage at Nicetown.

The covers had been turned down on her bed and Katharine wished she could crawl between the sheets and pull the soft comforter about her shoulders. But if she did that, she would miss the prayers. And if she let Elizabeth catch her yawning, her eight-year-old sister would insist that Katharine go to bed.

Outside the cottage, the first autumn winds were rustling the leaves. Katharine bent over her doll's crib to pull a blanket over the little figure.

"You'll be sure to catch cold," she sighed. Then one by one she admired the tiny garments in her favorite doll's clothes chest.

When the girls' father finally came upstairs, he was alone. He made an excuse for their mother but, by that time, both sisters were too sleepy to even question. A few moments after blessing themselves, they were fast asleep.

Francis A. Drexel was a millionaire but, as he pulled the

covers about his daughters, he mused that all the money in the world was nothing compared with them. He knelt beside the bed and offered another prayer for God's protection on his children and, "especially tonight," on his wife.

In years to come, Katharine and Elizabeth would remember that night when their father had been late for night prayers because of what happened the next morning. It was the second day of October 1863, and it seemed like the middle of the night when a nurse came to their room.

"The angels were here last night," she began, "and they brought…"

"What did they bring?" The girls sat up in bed wide-eyed.

"They brought your mother and father and you a baby—a little baby girl." The nurse laughed as the children bounded out of bed and ran to their mother's room.

But the sight of their mother lying so pale and quiet made them forget about the baby. Katharine and Elizabeth stood at the door until Mrs. Drexel spoke.

"Don't you want to see your little sister?" she asked when she opened her eyes.

Katharine put her hand in Elizabeth's and the two solemnly walked over to inspect the tiny, wriggling baby.

That's when Katharine noticed the blanket wrapped about the infant and the little dress. "My doll's clothes!" she cried with delight. "She's wearing my doll's clothes!"

"Yes, dear." Mrs. Drexel smiled. "The angels brought their gift before we were expecting her. So, we had to borrow a few things from your doll. Aunt Elizabeth has already gone to the city to shop for the baby. You don't mind the baby using your doll's clothes, do you?"

Katharine beamed. She didn't mind in the least. It made her feel closer to the new baby who, only two days later, on the feast of Saint Francis Assisi, was christened Louise Bouvier Drexel.

From then on, life in the Drexel household revolved around Elizabeth, Katharine, and Louise. Each was precious in her own way to Mr. Drexel who, with his brother Anthony, headed the international banking firm founded by their shrewd and talented father, Francis Martin Drexel.

Mrs. Drexel, the former Emma Bouvier, showered such affection on the children one would never have guessed she was actually Katharine and Elizabeth's stepmother. The two girls had been born of Francis Drexel's first marriage to Hannah Jane Langstroth. Katharine was born on November 26, 1858, and Hannah died just five weeks later.

Katharine was a little over a year old and Elizabeth had just turned three when their father remarried. With the silent help of Eliza Langstroth, their grandmother, Emma did all she could to keep the two little girls from ever feeling that they were not her own.

Katharine Mary, as she had been baptized, was already answering to the name of Kate when a young Irish girl, Johanna Ryan, joined the Drexel household to help care for the girls. "Joe," as she was affectionately called, had been a novice at the nearby Eden Hall Convent, but poor health had forced her to leave.

During the winter months, the Drexels lived at 1503 Walnut Street, a handsome residence in the fashionable quarter of Philadelphia. Because of Mr. Drexel's position as a banker, prominent businessmen from all over the world were frequent visitors. His wife was a gracious hostess, but her family and her various charities were always her first concern.

Though the word "stepmother" was never used, Emma Drexel never attempted to keep Katharine and Elizabeth from knowing that they were not her own children. Each Saturday afternoon Joe took the girls to the home of their Grandmother Langstroth, who had a special room furnished with toys for her grandchildren.

On another day each week Mrs. Drexel took all three of the girls for a visit with their Grandmother Bouvier, her mother, who was said to be "as stately a dame as ever graced the court of Versailles." Their Grandfather Bouvier had come to Philadelphia from his birthplace of Pont-Saint-Esprit, France, and the French influence was evident in the Bouvier and Drexel households.

Though there was only a three years' difference between Elizabeth and Kate, the bond between Kate and Louise seemed even closer.

The three sisters loved to listen to the family stories Mrs. Drexel often told. They also thrilled at the adventures of the saints. Despite their luxurious surroundings, the Drexel girls developed a special devotion to Saint Francis, the "Poor Little Man" of Assisi. It was usually Kate who begged hardest to hear the stories about Francis' love of the poor, animals, and nature. Each time she heard how young Francis sold his father's goods to raise enough money to repair the Church of San Damiano, Kate put herself in his place. She wondered what her own father would have said if she had sold one of the treasured paintings done by her grandfather, or the beloved pipe organ with the beautiful rosewood console, in order to obtain money for the poor who were always coming to her mother for help.

The time came all too soon when storytelling had to give way to the more serious business of school. Kate was secretly envious on that first day when her mother took Elizabeth to the Walnut Street school of the Religious of the Sacred Heart. She brooded and lagged about the house. Even when Louise begged for "just one little trick," her suddenly solemn older sister paid no attention.

That afternoon Kate was awakening from a long nap when her mother arrived with an invitation. Would Kate like to go with her to call for Elizabeth at the school?

Kate was delighted. Joe helped her get dressed quickly and in a few moments, they were on their way. This was the beginning of a happy custom. Each afternoon Joe stayed with Louise while Kate and her mother picked up Elizabeth.

In due time Kate followed in Elizabeth's steps, joining her older sister at school.

When Elizabeth made her first Holy Communion, Kate too wanted to receive and began talking about "the happiest day of my life." At that time, it was the norm for children to make their First Communion around the age of twelve. However, Kate expressed such longing to receive the Holy Eucharist that Mrs. Drexel and the sisters at the school agreed to allow her this privilege on June 3, 1870, while she was still eleven.

The Religious of the Sacred Heart made great preparation for the day. Kate and all of the first communicants were to be confirmed immediately after the Mass at which they had received the Eucharist for the first time. Mrs. Drexel would treat the girls and their mothers to a Communion breakfast at which Archbishop Wood of Philadelphia was to be the guest of honor.

"I wonder if heaven is like this," Kate whispered to Elizabeth when they caught a glimpse of the school chapel before the ceremony. The altar was radiant with candles and a light scent of freshly-cut flowers filled the air. Kate welcomed her Lord into her heart that day with inexpressible love and joy. It was the beginning of the intimate Eucharistic relationship that would characterize all of her long life.

It wasn't long before Kate and her sisters came to understand that their father was a very important man to many people. Board meetings were often held at the Drexel home, and financiers like J. R. Morgan of Wall Street fame, and E. T. Stotesbury of the Philadelphia banking clan, were among the many who visited frequently.

His business appointments never kept Francis Drexel from joining his family for night prayers when he was home, however. And once a month, he led them up the church aisle to Communion. (Then it was unheard of for people to receive the Eucharist more often.)

During the winter, when the family lived in Philadelphia, Mr. Drexel went directly to his room upon returning from the bank each afternoon. He would close the door and stay there for some time. Later, when they heard beautiful melodies pouring from the music room, the family knew that Mr. Drexel was at his beloved pipe organ.

While Mr. Drexel was in his room, neither Mrs. Drexel nor the girls dared to disturb him. One day, when Kate was tiptoeing past, a maid noticed her. "He's not asleep," she whispered.

"Isn't he?" Kate asked. She had always thought that her father rested when he came home from work.

The maid shook her head. "No. But I'm the only one who knows what he does in there. If you promise not to tell a soul, I'll tell you. Follow me down to the pantry."

Kate was a bit worried because it seemed the servant had spied on her father. She wasn't at all sure it was right. And she wasn't sure, either, that she could promise not to tell her mother. But the maid didn't wait for Kate's promise.

"I'd forgotten whether I'd finished my dusting or not," she

explained in a whisper, "so I rushed to his room thinking I'd get it done before he came home from the bank. But wouldn't you know *that* would be the day Mr. Drexel had come home early? I opened the door and there he was—the Mister himself—on his knees praying. He was praying so hard, mind you, that he never even heard the sound I made when I opened the door. I was so surprised to see him, you know. And I've been back since, always accidental like—not to spy—and he's doing the same thing: praying."

Kate's first summers were spent at Nicetown where Louise had been born. It was considered the country then, but today it falls within the city limits of Philadelphia. There, on Fishers Lane, was a comfortable house, which Mr. Drexel rented from Mrs. Susan Ole. The Drexels went out to Fishers Lane in the late spring, remaining through the summer until the trees were aglow with their autumn hues.

Mrs. Ole lived in a cottage at the rear of the main house. She kept a large vegetable garden, chickens, a cow, pigs, and a dog or two. It was here that Kate and her sisters came to know and love animals.

Shooing the chickens and racing the dogs was fun, but Jenny and Dap, two donkeys who pulled the girls' little cart, were the most popular. Each morning the pair announced the dawn of a new day with their gentle braying. At breakfast, two shaggy heads were thrust inside the open dining room window and the donkey serenade continued, until Mr. Drexel or the girls offered bits of bread from the table.

The Fishers Lane house was lighted by kerosene lamps and

the task of fetching the oil from the store fell to Kate and Elizabeth. Jenny and Dap always transported them in the cart. As payment, the girls were allowed to treat themselves to old-fashioned ginger cookies. The most exciting part of the excursion began after the donkeys had trotted past an old mill, the last object that could be seen from the porch of their house. Then Elizabeth would give the signal and the two girls would straddle the donkeys.

On their return trip, the adventure was sometimes interrupted when the cart would hit a rut in the road and kerosene would slosh through the spout of the can onto the cookies. Then the only thing to do was to stop at the next water pump, wash the cookies off, and eat them all before the oil had time to soak in!

Kate was never sure what she should do when mischievous boys trotted along beside the donkeys and then jumped into the empty seat while the girls rode astride. She knew, though, that Elizabeth would make sure her whip was in plain view when she called, "Get out, please. Get out at once!" The boys always obeyed. Elizabeth knew how to speak with authority.

Every day after lunch the girls took a nap. Once afternoon prayers had been said, Mrs. Drexel would read to them until they drifted off to sleep. Sometimes Kate dreamed about Saint Francis and faraway Assisi. At other times, George Washington, another of her heroes, was the subject of her dreams. More than once she went to sleep whispering, "Let perpetual light shine upon George Washington. May his soul rest in peace." It was a practice she was to continue for the rest of her life.

Kate loved to get dressed up late in the afternoon and wait for her father on the side porch of Mrs. Ole's house. Once he was home, the family would often go for a carriage drive until supper.

But life at Fishers Lane also had its unpleasant side for young Kate. She dreaded sewing lessons, and the tedious hours of piano practice weren't to her liking either.

Looking back many years later, it seemed to Kate that 1870, her twelfth year, was one of the most eventful of her early life. The nation was still in the midst of troubled times growing out of the War Between the States, which Kate had been too young to remember. To Katharine Drexel, 1870 recalled not the memory of the bitter Reconstruction Era, but thoughts of her First Communion and of the service of Mary Ann Cassidy, who was to tutor the Drexel girls at home.

Miss Cassidy resided with her widowed mother and sister in Camden, New Jersey, just across the Delaware River. Mrs. Drexel had described her as "a lovely young woman—well educated and really exceptional."

Mr. Drexel wasn't opposed to the idea of a tutor, but he wondered whether the daily trip across the river might prove too difficult for Miss Cassidy. It didn't. And so began Mary Ann Cassidy's long and happy association with the Drexel family.

It was also in 1870 that Francis Drexel bought a ninety-acre farm on the Red Lion Road at Torresdale, Pennsylvania, which was to be called Saint Michel's (the French rendering of Saint Michael's).

Before the girls saw it, Mr. Drexel enlarged and remodeled the three-story house. A roofed porch was built across the entire front of the house. At one end of the porch was a big Dutch door, the glass of the upper part protected on the outside by elaborately wrought iron grillwork.

Above the front door, Mr. Drexel had mounted a statue of Saint Michael, his spear, and a shield carved in Caen stone. A mosaic floor was laid just inside the entrance. To the right was a drawing room and then large folding doors, which opened to reveal a spacious and beautiful dining room.

At the head of the first flight of stairs was a recessed window. Because the house had been placed under the special guardianship of Saint Michael, Uncle Michel Bouvier's patron saint, Mr. Drexel commissioned a stained glass window representing the archangel.

The Drexels always used the French pronunciation in speaking of the Torresdale home. Joe Ryan was the only one who refused to follow suit. "No Ryan would call Saint Michael anything but 'Michael'!" she insisted.

The sprawling grounds around the house were converted into well-kept lawns with shade trees. Cottages were built for servants, as well as a spacious stable, carriage house, and barn.

Francis Drexel and his wife spared neither time nor money in furnishing and decorating the interior of the house. Mrs. Drexel chose a special day for her three daughters and Joe to have their first glimpse of the country estate.

After her speech about the name, Joe had nothing but praise for Saint Michel's. "And sure it's just like a palace," she insisted. "Fit for any king or queen—or princesses," she added when she saw the expression on the girls' faces.

Soon after the Drexels occupied Saint Michel's, Mrs. Drexel suggested a plan that made Kate very happy.

Chapter 2

The Mountains Cast a Shadow

Elizabeth and Kate were to share a bedroom at Saint Michel's, just as they did in their city home. Miss Cassidy gently hinted that perhaps it was time fourteen-year-old Elizabeth had a room of her own.

"That will come later," Mrs. Drexel replied. "Kate is too young to be alone yet, and if I put Louise in with her, there will be no sleeping. I'd really like Kate to spend more time with Elizabeth," she added thoughtfully. "There are times when she amazes me with the seriousness of her thoughts—especially in spiritual matters. Her devotion to Saint Francis of Assisi has given her a burning desire to help the poor."

"Her devotion to Saint Francis, yes, and the beautiful example set by her own mother and father," Miss Cassidy declared with feeling.

"God has been good to us," Emma Drexel responded simply. "We must share that over which he has made us guardians and never forget our responsibility to others, especially our employees." Then she went on to unfold her plan for the two older girls.

Saint Michel's had settled into stillness. Prayers had been said and Joe was in Louise's room putting her to bed when Mrs. Drexel slipped into the older girls' room.

"You look so mysterious, Mama," Elizabeth observed after they had talked for a while. "I hope Miss Cassidy isn't going to scold us about our spelling."

Mrs. Drexel put an arm around each of her girls. "Few mothers have been blessed with such wonderful daughters. That's why I decided on the plan I'm now going to tell you about."

Kate's thoughts raced along as she tried to imagine what her mother was going to tell them. *Perhaps,* she thought, *we're old enough now to help give out clothes and groceries to the people who come to our back door for help. We've wanted to do that for so long. But we're at Saint Michel's now, and Mama wouldn't tell us about that until we're in the city again. Surely, she's not going to tell us that it's time we were going away to school.*

"You need not worry about your spelling for the moment, Elizabeth. And you can erase that frown, Kate," Mrs. Drexel went on smiling. "Seriously, I've been concerned about the children of the men and women who work for us. There are no sisters nearby to instruct them, and I feel a grave responsibility because we brought several of the families out from the city. I was hoping that you girls would help me to start a Sunday school."

Elizabeth threw her arms about her mother's neck. "No one ever had such a wonderful mother!" she declared. "You think of everyone's welfare. We'd love to teach Sunday school, wouldn't we, Kate?"

"Oh, yes!" Kate exclaimed. She was so happy she could hardly speak. "Yes!" Hadn't Saint Francis gone out to preach and teach the people? Now she would really be following in his footsteps.

For the next few days, Kate and Elizabeth were busy with plans. A section of the laundry room was set aside for classes. It was agreed that Kate would teach the younger girls and Elizabeth would instruct the older ones.

"Don't you think boys have souls, too?" their father teased.

"The decision to start with the girls was mine," Mrs. Drexel admitted. "Of course the boys have souls, but they can also be more stubborn at times—boys young or old," and here the wife gave her husband a knowing glance, "might not want to come to Sunday school just because they're told to do so. With the girls there, the boys will be sure to come around—even if it's just to see what's happening."

In less than a month, almost fifty children were crowding into the laundry room on Sunday afternoons. After the lesson, Kate led them up to the parlor where Elizabeth took her place at the piano and they sang their favorite hymns. Kate had never enjoyed practicing the piano, or taking vocal lessons, but after the initiation of the religion classes, she was grateful that her mother had insisted.

Miss Cassidy was very proud of her two oldest pupils. She had made a rule some time before that during the summer, when there were no classes, the girls should write her twice a week. So, Miss Cassidy stayed abreast of her pupils' vacation activities while at the same time keeping a check on the quality of their writing. That summer the letters were full of news of the Sunday school.

In the early fall of 1870, a letter from Kate told of some added excitement. Archbishop Wood was to pay a visit to the Drexel country home!

Not until the day of the archbishop's visit did Mrs. Drexel tell the girls that their visitor would celebrate Mass at Saint Michel's the following morning. A carriage was ordered to take Joe and Kate over to Eden Hall—Mrs. Drexel's sister Louise was a Religious of the Sacred Heart at the convent there. Her superior had agreed to supply the altar linens and sacred vessels.

"It's sure a great honor," Joe kept telling Kate, "to have the archbishop himself sleeping under the same roof with you. But to have the Holy Mass said right in your own parlor—that's really something! Only a few people would ever get that permission. But then, the Drexels are very special. People all over Philadelphia talk about the good work they do."

The news spread quickly, and the next morning the folding doors of the dining room had to be opened. The parlor was too small for the family and all the workmen who came to the special Eucharistic celebration.

The next big event at Saint Michel's was the closing session of Sunday school. Miss Cassidy had suggested in one of her letters that the pupils be given badges or prizes for attendance and application. Mrs. Drexel offered to buy prizes, and the last Sunday at Saint Michel's was selected for the awards ceremony.

It was while her middle daughter was making the list for gifts to be given out to the Sunday school pupils that Mrs. Drexel decided Kate had inherited some of her father's shrewdness and practical way of thinking.

Elizabeth was growing to look more and more like the Langstroths, who were Dutch. Her complexion, hair, and eyes were lighter than Kate's or Louise's. While, from the time she was a toddler, Louise's striking resemblance to her mother was obvious to everyone. As she grew older, her blond curls were richer in hue and her thin lips a bit less severe than her mother's. Still, she was a small replica of Emma Drexel.

Kate, instead, was "Papa's girl." Like her father, she had a determined chin, and deep-set, thoughtful blue eyes. She also had her father's finely chiseled nose, but where his was straight, there was the slightest tilt at the extreme end of Kate's.

"Only about half of the children came every Sunday," Kate told her mother as she made out the Sunday school gift list, "so only the faithful need be rewarded."

"Don't be mean," Elizabeth spoke up. "We can give something to them all. Mama said we could."

"It would be wrong to encourage those who came only when they felt like it," Kate insisted seriously. "Mama said we could serve cookies and lemonade after the prizes are given out. Then nobody will be left out. But we can't encourage the lazy ones, can we?"

Mrs. Drexel agreed with Kate, though she tried to conceal her surprise. She was also surprised when Kate selected practical prizes like pencil boxes, gloves, and prayer books.

All of the Drexels felt a twinge of regret when it finally came time to leave Saint Michel's and return to the city. Most of the city servants went ahead to Philadelphia to prepare for the family's return. Since Mr. Drexel was at work, Mrs. Drexel, the girls, and Joe were left to follow in the carriage with what pets they were allowed to bring home, the more valuable table silver, and assorted bundles. The enjoyable trip took away some of the sting of leaving their summer home.

Each fall, soon after returning to 1503 Walnut Street, Mr. Drexel would take the family for a short trip to a different part of the United States he thought would prove interesting to the girls.

"It's easier to learn history and geography by traveling," he reminded Miss Cassidy, who was afraid the trips might interfere with the girls' studies.

While California, Maine, Colorado, the Great Lakes region, New Orleans, and the White Mountains were merely names on the map to most students, they became wonderful memories for Kate and her sisters. The White Mountains seemed to offer Kate the most satisfying adventures. In one of her biweekly letters to Miss Cassidy, Kate detailed an incident from their trip. It was a Sunday morning and the family had set out for a climb to Thompson's Falls where they planned to say their morning prayers. Kate and Louise ran on ahead of Elizabeth and their parents.

"Anybody can find the way to Thompson's Falls," Louise grumbled as she stopped to tear a briar from her heavy sock. "I wish we could go to Tuckerman's Ravine. The guidebook says it's spooky there."

"I wish we could, too," Kate sighed. "But the guidebook also says that the path is blind and difficult and that children should be left at home."

"I've been to Thompson's Falls before," Louise pouted as she broke into a trot, "and I don't want to go there today."

Suddenly they reached a fork in the road. "One of these paths leads to Tuckerman's Ravine," Kate half whispered. "And the other leads to the Falls. But I can't remember which one. We'd better wait till the others catch up with us."

"Oh come on," Louise urged. "It won't be long before they'll be calling to us to wait anyway." And the two girls took the road that led up the side of the mountain.

Soon they heard a familiar call. They turned to see Elizabeth running to catch up with them.

"Papa is furious!" she announced breathlessly. "A man just came along who knows this country and he said we're on the road to Tuckerman's Ravine. He's going there, too, and he offered to guide us. Mama wants to go, but Papa says he couldn't take you two on such a dangerous climb."

"The guidebook did say the road was marked by flares,"

Kate remembered. "Maybe that will change his mind. We'll tell Mama."

The three headed back toward their parents. They found the volunteer guide busy reassuring Mr. Drexel. This gave Kate and Louise time to talk privately with their mother.

"Oh, Mama," Kate begged, "can't you convince Papa to let us continue the climb?"

"This man," Mrs. Drexel whispered, "seems to be handling the job himself. He just told you're father he's sure the path is marked by flares. Perhaps we will get to see the ravine after all."

The conference was interrupted by the booming voice of the guide. "We'll take the first turn to the left, ladies, then up we'll go!"

They followed moss-covered pathways, crossed creeks and streams that seemed to appear suddenly and end just as abruptly. Kate was puzzled when she first saw her father pull a piece of paper from his pocket, tear it into bits, and fasten these onto the trees. But she realized, almost immediately, what he was doing.

As they crawled over a pile of fallen hemlocks, Louise, too, noticed her father.

"What's he doing with the paper?" she whispered to Kate.

"Marking the trail."

"What for? He's not afraid, is he?"

"Papa is never afraid," Kate declared. As they jumped across a smaller pile of broken hemlocks, she told her sister about a day at the seashore when she had been standing on the beach afraid to go into the water. Mr. Drexel had swung her over his shoulders and waded out into the surf.

"I had my arms tightly around Papa's neck," she continued. "The salt spray splashed into my face and I choked a little. Papa ducked, and as I went under the water, he met a great wave. It dashed against us then covered us both. I thought I was drowning. I closed my eyes and held onto Papa's neck as tightly as I could. I could feel Papa's arms around me, and when he told me to open my eyes, we were safe on the beach again. I told him how strong his arms were, and he said our heavenly Father's arms were around both of us, and that's what saved us."

"Maybe he just doesn't think the Lord's arms will reach up here and keep us from getting lost," Louise suggested with a grin.

"Shame on you!" Kate scolded. "How dare you say such a thing!"

"Oh, Kate, you know I was only teasing. You used to be so much fun. You're just becoming too sancti...sancti.... What's that big word Joe said you were getting to be?"

"So you and Joe have been talking about me?" Kate laughed.

"I know!" Louise cried. "Joe said you were getting *sanctimonious* and that I shouldn't worry because I'm not. Joe says she doesn't think I ever will be."

Kate wondered why Joe had said she was *sanctimonious*. Only her mother knew about her love for Saint Francis and her daily practice of asking God to look kindly on the soul of George Washington. Still her mother always turned to her when she wanted Louise coached on prayers or proper behavior at Mass. Kate wondered if Joe had said Elizabeth was sanctimonious, too.

The girls walked along in silence for another mile, pushing back the thick bushes in their path. The rest of the party followed a few feet behind. The sisters hadn't even noticed that flares no longer marked the path until they heard their father's voice rise above that of the volunteer guide.

"I'm not going another step!" Mr. Drexel insisted. "I didn't want to come, but you assured me you knew the path. I will not jeopardize the safety of my family."

"I told you he wasn't afraid," Kate whispered to Louise. "He's thinking only of us."

Elizabeth called to her sisters. "Mama is sure we can sight the flares," she said, "if only we go a little farther. Kate, come with me, Mama will take Louise. We'll stay within calling distance. That poor man doesn't know what a stone wall Papa can be. They'll be arguing for a while, but if we find the path, there'll be no objection to going on."

Mrs. Drexel and the girls disappeared among the thickets while her husband and the guide continued to argue.

Within minutes, a triumphant shout rang through the trees.

"We've sighted the flares again!" Mrs. Drexel cried.

"We've spotted them, too!" Kate echoed. "Come, Papa, we'll be sure to find the path now."

"You've also lost the bottom of your skirt." Her father pointed to a torn flounce. "And you've scratched your face. We're not going another step!"

Kate knew her father's mind was made up. Nothing would change it.

"Let's say our prayers by those rocks," she suggested, pointing to a small chain of boulders. Elizabeth and Louise followed her.

The sight of the kneeling children fingering their beads and their young voices in prayer softened Mr. Drexel's scowl and dulled his wife's disappointment. The guide continued on his way while the parents joined the children. Together they praised the heavenly Father whose strong arms were always around them.

The descent was made easier by the pieces of paper Mr. Drexel had fastened onto the trees. The sun was already setting when they glimpsed the hotel. Without any spoken agreement, the group stopped to look up at the peaks before them—Mounts Madison, Jefferson, Adams, Clay, and Washington.

Kate edged closer to her mother. "They're so big and bold," she whispered. "Even the sunset can't soften them. They're like the time that was and the time that will be."

"Yes," her mother answered softly, "like the solidarity of eternity."

"That's what Miss Cassidy said one day when we were talking about mountains—that they make you think of eternity. Before," Kate admitted, "it was always hard for me to think of what eternity meant. Now I'm beginning to understand. It just means the time that was and the time that will be—forever and ever."

Mrs. Drexel nodded and smiled.

Chapter 3

European Tour

It was the winter of 1874 and Kate was sixteen when her parents made plans for a family trip to Europe.

Kate was happy with the idea but worried about the Sunday school classes at Saint Michel's.

"I'm sure we won't leave until fall." Elizabeth reassured her. "Joe told me the other day that she's going with us. That means Miss Cassidy will stay behind to take charge of the house, and we won't have to bother about lessons while we're in Europe. Isn't that wonderful?"

"The only real difference," practical Kate reminded her sister, "is that we'll be writing our lessons in the form of letters—twice a week!"

Kate was right. A few days later their mother showed them a note from Miss Cassidy about the letters she expected to receive from Europe. Elizabeth moaned. "Kate will describe every cathedral and every shrine in Europe, and Miss Cassidy will consider it a matter of conscience to give her good marks, no matter how dull the letters are."

Kate said nothing. *Just as well*, she thought. *It's better that I hadn't told Elizabeth how badly I wanted to visit the Vatican and Assisi.*

"I should remind you, girls," Mrs. Drexel went on, "since

we're speaking of classes, I've asked Mademoiselle de Saint Marsault to double up on your French lessons. Once you're in Europe you'll appreciate being able to speak another language."

One rainy afternoon at Saint Michel's, when Mr. Drexel was late returning from the city, Mrs. Drexel entertained the girls by recounting some of her honeymoon adventures in Europe.

She told them all about stopping at Pont-Saint-Esprit, France, to visit the Bouvier relatives. Then it was on to Dirnborn, Austria, the birthplace of Mr. Drexel's father, Francis Martin Drexel. On the wall inside his old home hung a beautiful depiction of the Blessed Virgin and Child, which their Grandfather Drexel had painted when he was a young man of eighteen. Mrs. Drexel told the girls about Ireland, Paris, and about that June day when she and their father had been presented to the Holy Father, Pius IX, in private audience. The kindly Pope had blessed their marriage.

Louise could hardly contain her excitement. "Mama," she finally broke in, "our appetite for Europe is *enormous!* When do we sail?"

"After we've all done an *enormous* amount of packing," her mother laughingly replied.

Mr. Drexel booked passage on the *Scotia* of the Cunard Line for the latter part of September 1874.

Joe, who was as excited as the girls over the trip, was furious when she heard that Liverpool was the first city they would visit.

"Who wants to go to *that* place?" she grumbled. "Ireland is the place for anyone to go who really wants to see something!" The only thing that served to calm her down was Mrs. Drexel's assurance that they would be spending only one day in London.

The girls left the shores of their native America in high spirits. While they were all seasoned land travelers, they suffered from a bit of seasickness the first few days of their journey. Once that difficulty was behind, they were free to enjoy the serenity of the ocean.

A visit to Westminster Abbey filled most of the day the Drexels spent in London. Mrs. Drexel gave Joe the option of remaining at the hotel to rest or of joining the family for the excursion to the abbey.

Joe insisted on going and confined her grumbling to the ears of the three girls. But she couldn't control her anger when the family group stopped in front of the tomb of Queen Elizabeth.

"Now, what would sensible people like the Drexels be doing," she muttered, "standing here looking at auld Betsy's monument?" And the loyal daughter of Erin went on to make a number of guesses as to the present whereabouts of "auld Betsy."

Later, as they stood in front of the tomb of one of the monks who had lived before the time of Henry VIII, Joe's anger broke out again. The sexton who was showing them through the abbey, weary from the task of deciphering inscribed names, referred to the deceased as a "jawbreaker." Mrs. Drexel saw the danger signal in Joe's eyes. "You girls walk ahead with Joe," she suggested. "We'll catch up with you in a little while."

The girls propelled the indignant Joe out of the sexton's hearing. "I wish the walls of the whole dingy place would fall on his head," she sputtered and fumed. "Why couldn't he call the good priest respectfully by his own name—the way *any* decent man would?"

"I'm glad to get out." Kate tried to change the subject. "All of these tombs make me think of a monument store."

"It serves you right." Joe wouldn't be sidetracked. "I still can't figure why anyone in his right mind would want to come to this place—not that I mean to be disrespectful of the Mister and Missus," she added.

The parents found the girls laughing when they rejoined them. Johanna had given the London visit a comical twist.

Mrs. Drexel and the girls were delighted when they reached Lausanne, Switzerland, to find an old friend from Baltimore, Miss Carrere, waiting for them at the hotel. Miss Carrere had been living in Italy for some years and because of her knowledge of the continent, Mr. Drexel had invited her to join the party.

"Caro," as the girls called her, knew of their father's love of the organ, and she led them to great cathedrals and musty little churches full of medieval statues where they heard wonderful organ music. This proved to be one of the greatest joys of the trip for Mr. Drexel.

The girls looked forward to seeing the famous clock when they visited Bern, and Louise was up before the rest of the family that first morning in the historic hometown of world-renowned Swiss watchmakers.

"Hurry!" she kept saying. "The procession of bears starts on the hour. There might be a crowd in front of the tower."

There were minutes to spare when the Drexels reached the clock tower. Only a few other people were waiting for the national procession. Then, at the stroke of twelve, the first of the miniature animals emerged from the clock. To Louise it was great fun, but Kate thought the performance childish.

In Vienna, Mr. Drexel escorted his two eldest daughters to the theater where they saw a presentation of *Oberon*. But, as Kate later confided to her teacher in what the girls called her "weekly agonizings," Vienna would always be remembered humorously because of another small excursion.

It didn't seem at all humorous though, the morning Kate and Elizabeth decided they would dare to set out alone—and unchaperoned—to find an English-speaking confessor.

"There's that little church not too far from the hotel," Kate remembered. "We can go to Mass and then inquire about a confessor. I do wish we could speak German though. How will we make them understand what we want?"

"We'll decide that later," assured Elizabeth, who was in a hurry to get started.

The girls decided Mass was either over or hadn't yet begun as they entered the almost empty church. They waited a while after they had prayed, then walked around the building until they found a door. It seemed to lead to the sacristy. A few gentle knocks brought no results. They knocked harder. Still no response. They hammered violently until a boy appeared, astonished at seeing two refined-looking young ladies who seemed bent upon knocking in the sacristy door.

Elizabeth walked over to the confessional, pointed to it and repeated in German "Is there an English-speaking priest?"

"He almost laughed," Kate whispered to Elizabeth when the boy had disappeared. "And you used the German pronunciation that Papa said was correct."

After a long wait the young sacristan reappeared and addressed the girls in rapid German which neither understood. They managed to catch the names of Saint Anne and Saint Catherine. Perhaps that meant there was an English-speaking priest at either of those churches.

"He might have gotten one of the priests for us," Elizabeth complained as they walked back to the hotel. "Now we'll have to look through the guidebooks to find out where those churches are."

Johanna Ryan loved nothing more than surmounting obstacles, so while the girls were looking through one guidebook, she found the Church of Saint Catherine listed in another. When they started out again, Joe was their accomplice.

A cross-looking sexton was locking the door when the trio arrived at Saint Catherine's. Once more Elizabeth asked for an English-speaking priest as her father had taught her. The old sexton shrugged his shoulders and slammed the door.

Again, they consulted the guidebook, then set out to find Saint Anne's. Someone mistook them for Italians and directed them to an Italian hospital at the opposite end of the city. Their next attempt landed the hapless three in a convent where they interrupted the nuns in the midst of community prayers. None of these good religious spoke or understood either English or the Drexel-Ryan brand of German.

After a number of attempts, Kate and her companions found the Monastery of Saint Anne. A kindly brother admitted them, listened to their request, and evidently took them for tourists. He conducted them through labyrinthian corridors until they reached an immense iron door, which squeaked with the rust of age when it was opened—the better for the three amazed girls to view the vault of Marie Antoinette!

At last, the little party returned to the hotel, but they were not yet ready to give up their search.

That religious was wearing the brown robe of Saint Francis, Kate kept thinking. *Somehow, I feel that Francis' brother will lead us to what we want.*

She confided this to Joe and Elizabeth, who agreed that it was too late to start out again, but that they would try the next morning.

The next day, Emma Drexel didn't think there was anything unusual about her girl's plans to go to Mass, but she could tell by the satisfied expression on Joe's face that *this* morning some new adventure was afoot. Knowing Joe to be a formidable chaperon, however, Mrs. Drexel had not a single fear for their safety.

Once more, the determined three made their way to the Monastery of Saint Anne. Once more Kate rang the bell, and once more, the same brother who had treated them to a view of Marie Antoinette's vault opened the door.

He gave a deep sigh and clasped his hands, looking heavenward as if for help to understand the request that Elizabeth repeated once again. He motioned to them to wait, and Kate felt confident that Saint Francis was interceding.

In a few moments the brother returned. He led them down a dimly lighted hall, which seemed to have no end, and turned into another just as long and just as dim.

"And whose tomb do you think he's taking us to this time?" Johanna's voice echoed through the silent corridor.

"Where's that undying faith you're always bragging about?" Elizabeth asked.

"Well," Joe grinned, "I'm holding my beads."

Kate put her finger to her lips and frowned at Joe and Elizabeth. Turning, she thought she saw a shadow and the flicker of a candle in the distance. The shadow walked toward them until they were face to face with a tall, elegant-looking priest whose handsome features and long, gray beard caught the warm glow of the candle he held in his hand. His piercing black eyes studied the eager faces before him.

"Americans?" he asked slowly.

"Yes, Father," Elizabeth began, only to be interrupted by Joe.

"They're the Drexels from Philadelphia," Joe rattled away. "The Holy Father himself gave Archbishop Wood permission to celebrate Mass at their house on Walnut Street *and* at the place in the country. Not only that, but the archbishop sleeps under the same roof with them when he comes out to the country to say the Holy Mass."

Kate was embarrassed, but she saw that the priest did not understand what Joe was saying. This time she was the one who stated their mission. In broken English, the priest haltingly explained that he did not understand their language well enough to hear confessions. Kate was beginning to think Saint Francis had failed her when the priest asked if they could speak French.

Once the confessions were over, the brother emerged from the darkness and led them through the long halls for the last time.

"No American priest's 'Go and sin no more' ever sounded more beautiful," Kate sighed.

"My French was no better than his English," Joe admitted. "I hope Saint Peter doesn't hold this confession against me on Judgment Day."

Kate longed to visit Assisi, but every time she mentioned it, something intervened before her parents could promise to make the trip. Her father was anxious to reach Italy, but he spoke only of visiting Florence and Rome. Kate, remembering Louis's comment that she was becoming too sanctimonious, decided to wait and say nothing more.

Soon after reaching Italy, the Drexels stopped overnight in Bologna. The next day they went for a tour of the city and, as they approached the Church of Saint Catherine, a guide told them that the relics of Saint Catherine were reposing there.

"Do you mean Saint Catherine of Siena?" Kate asked. "She's my patron saint."

"Yes, yes!" the man answered. "Saint Catherine is there—seated on a chair. Would you like to pray before her? I will see if arrangements can be made to open the small chapel."

Kate was thrilled at the prospect of viewing the body of her patron saint and took out her beads to offer up a rosary of thanksgiving. She had barely finished a decade when the guide returned with a priest who smiled and bowed as he led them to a little chapel where he opened the door with a huge key which hung at his waist.

Only four candles illuminated the chapel, and on the altar sat the incorrupt body of Saint Catherine. The Drexels stared in wonderment.

The priest bowed to them again before he genuflected and disappeared.

"The body was placed here ten years after her death," the guide whispered. "It was never embalmed and is just as limber as it was 450 years ago."

"Look." He pointed to a red spot on the lips of the figure whose face and hands, even though they had turned black, remained firm and unwrinkled. "That is the spot where our Lord kissed her."

It was only after Kate and her family had returned to the hotel, looked through their guidebooks, and talked with the chambermaid, that they discovered the saint they had seen was not Catherine of Siena but Catherine of Bologna.

"I've never heard of Saint Catherine of Bologna," Kate told her mother.

"Then perhaps it was a lesson well worth learning," Mrs. Drexel replied, knowing full well the sting of Kate's disappointment.

Later Kate thought again of the visit to Saint Catherine's chapel. *Perhaps I set too much store in earthly reminders of the saints*, she concluded. *After all, the important thing is that the saints are glorified in heaven and that we can pray to them no matter where we are. Maybe that's why Papa hasn't said anything else about visiting Assisi.*

On December 8, 1874, the Drexel family observed the feast of the Immaculate Conception in Florence. That afternoon they drove through olive fields ripe with purple fruit to the Chartreuse Monastery.

Kate thought she had never seen so picturesque a sight as the high wall that encircled the grounds. It was covered with roses, and now and then, they passed an opening in the wall through which they could see the majestic Apennines.

"To see these venerable old monks pacing the cloisters with their white cowls drawn over their heads," Elizabeth wrote Miss Cassidy, "or to hear them chanting the Office in the old walnut choir, just as they did 500 years ago, seemed more like something to be read and wondered about, than to be actually witnessed."

Mr. and Mrs. Drexel listened as the girls talked about the old monastery. Louise wished she could paint a picture of the monks praying the Divine Office. The evidence of the monks' good housekeeping impressed Elizabeth. She surprised them all when she soberly announced, "If I were a man, I would enter the order on the spot. But I would want access to a good library and a suite of rooms with a view of the Apennines."

"That," Mrs. Drexel declared, "is probably why you would not enter the order—even if you were a man. I have yet to hear of an order which induces would-be novices with good books and idyllic views."

The Drexels spent the Christmas of 1874 in Naples. Accustomed to snow and cold at Christmas, they found it difficult to get into the spirit of the season. As warm sunshine stole into the hotel windows, and as they watched the glistening blue waves of the bay, it seemed more like a holiday at the beach than a Christmas away from home.

"It will only make you appreciate next Christmas at Saint Michel's more," Mrs. Drexel told her homesick daughters.

The girls would always remember the colorful Christmas Eve celebrations in Naples. Against a velvety blue Italian sky studded with stars, hundreds of rockets ascended heavenward, while showers of tiny red, blue, and green lights were thrown from the balconies into the streets below. From their hotel suite, they could hear voices singing in the distance. The music reminded Kate of stories about the carefree days of Saint Francis' life when he expressed himself in serenades.

The New Year of 1875 found Kate and her family in Rome for the long-awaited visit to the Vatican. Mr. Drexel made the acquaintance of a helpful French priest who arranged for them to have an audience with the Holy Father. Johanna, as excited as the girls over the prospect of actually seeing the pope, asked Mrs. Drexel, again and again, about her visit to the Vatican during her honeymoon.

The priest who acted as their guide suggested that they bring a new silk skullcap which Louise, as the youngest member of the family, could present to the Holy Father. He also suggested that the family address the Pontiff in French.

On the morning of the audience, Mr. Drexel borrowed a silver tray from the hotel on which the white silk skullcap was placed. Then the family proceeded to the Vatican where their priest guide showed them through the various anterooms and halls leading to the small chamber where the audience was to be held.

Kate's parents were pleased at the dignified manner in which the girls and Joe behaved, despite their excitement at the spectacle of ornately dressed Swiss guards bearing the pope through the halls in his *sedia gestatoria*—a kind of portable throne carried on the shoulders—before setting him down in their midst.

When Pope Pius IX came to the Drexel group, Louise stepped forward, offered the skullcap, and said in her best French, "Very Holy Father, will you accept this cap and give me yours?"

Pope Pius IX laughingly replied in English, "But why do you want my cap? See. The one you brought me is too thin, too small. What would you do with mine—put it in your pocket?"

"Oh, no." Louise replied without prompting. "I want to take it home with me—to America!"

As she spoke, the delighted Pontiff playfully tossed his cap onto Louise's head and made as if to pass on. It was then that Joe, in a fit of enthusiasm, fell to the floor, pressed forward, and threw her arms around the Holy Father's knees as she cried, "Holy Father—praise God and his blessed Mother—my eyes have seen our dear Lord himself!"

Joe had acted impulsively—out of her unquestioning faith and intense devotion. She was so sincere and deeply moved that neither Mr. nor Mrs. Drexel mentioned the incident until some time later, and they forbade the girls to bring up the event.

En route to Paris the family stopped at Pont-Saint-Esprit, the birthplace of Mrs. Drexel's father, Michel Bouvier. There they participated at Mass in the same small church where he had worshipped.

When they reached Paris, Kate was delighted to see the ease with which the French included religion in their everyday lives. She admired their habit of frequently stopping into a church for a visit to the Blessed Sacrament.

As the trip continued, the family teased Kate because of her insistence that when she went shopping she never could find what she wanted. Despite the many beautiful clothes and objects d'art in Parisian shop windows, Kate claimed that the dress, coat, hat or picture she wanted always seemed to have been sold or was missing. They also called her "the flag waver" because she always compared sights, customs, and even shops to those of America.

It was only after Mr. Drexel announced that he thought it was time for Elizabeth to make her debut that the girls went on the shopping spree their mother had anticipated. Even then, Kate and Louise, who had some years to wait before being introduced to the social world, showed a preference for country clothes over the high fashion of Paris. In the end, it was a letter from Miss Cassidy that helped Mrs. Drexel to arouse an interest in feminine frills in her younger girls.

"Miss Cassidy writes that the city is agog with plans for the celebration of the one hundredth anniversary of the Declaration of Independence," Mrs. Drexel announced one morning at breakfast. "The exposition will be held next year."

"And we have decided," her husband added, "to wait until January of the centenary year, Elizabeth, to present you to society. With visitors in the city for the centennial, the occasion should be more festive. Though it is not a thought I relish," and Mr. Drexel's eyes twinkled, "it is highly possible that more than one or two eligible young men will present themselves at 1503 Walnut Street. I suppose I'll have to start looking with new eyes at my friends who have sons."

Elizabeth blushed, but Kate seemed little impressed. Louise was the only one of the three who spoke out. "Boys," she decided, "are not half as much fun as you, Papa. And as long as we have you and Uncle Michel and Uncle Tony and our cousins, it doesn't matter whether other boys come to our house or not!"

Mrs. Drexel smiled. She knew how much Louise's childish declaration of loyalty and devotion had pleased her husband. She knew, too, though, that Louise was going through a stage that would soon pass. Elizabeth was already showing an interest in young men. But she wasn't sure about Kate.

The double lure of Elizabeth's debut and the centennial awakened the girls' interest in clothes. And, in spite of the snow and cold weather that slowed the carriages on the streets of Paris during the winter of 1875, Kate and her sisters bought everything their mother thought a "well-outfitted young lady should have."

In the midst of the shopping, Kate thought from time to time of Saint Francis. They had not visited Assisi after all. She thought of how he had cast aside his fine clothes and rejoiced in poverty. Sometimes these thoughts made her uneasy. She felt no regret when her parents decided to forego visits to Scotland and Ireland and return to her beloved America.

Chapter 4

The Centennial

By June, Kate and her family were back at Saint Michel's. Recollections of the trip were a daily topic, and Kate made a packet of the pictures of famous castles, churches, and museums they had visited. After classes began again in the fall, she showed them to Miss Cassidy, along with the leaves and flowers she had plucked from various palace gardens and monuments.

Some weeks later, Miss Cassidy handed Kate a large package containing all the letters—edited and corrected—which her pupil had written from Europe. Kate copied them and put the collection in a scrapbook, illustrated with the pictures and pressed leaves and flowers. Mrs. Drexel told Miss Cassidy later how pleased she was that Kate had made the scrapbook.

"Once Kate begins a project," Miss Cassidy smilingly replied, "she seldom, if ever, stops until it's completed. In fact, she applies herself so well that sometimes she overdoes things."

"When she's happy, she's very happy," Mrs. Drexel said, "but when she's serious, she's very serious. She seems to go from one extreme to the other. I only hope we can help her to find her vocation in life without too much delay. Kate is nearly seventeen now, and a mother always wants to see her children established before..." Mrs. Drexel broke off and sighed, "before she leaves them."

49

After the Drexel's return to Philadelphia, preparations were begun for Elizabeth's introduction to society. Louise joked at Elizabeth's "new grown-up ways," but Kate felt a vague, inexpressible sadness at the absence of her older sister from the classroom.

As the Christmas before the centennial approached, there was much talk about the previous sunny Christmas in Naples. Their Walnut Street home had been redecorated, and greetings and laughter of friends and relatives echoed through the elegant rooms.

Kate and Elizabeth were pleased to help their mother prepare gifts for the needy. The family referred to Mrs. Drexel's habitual practice of helping scores of people who came to their back door as the "Dorcas," in memory of Dorcas in the Acts of the Apostles who had "devoted herself to good works and charity."

Mrs. Drexel even kept a woman regularly employed to care for the needy who sought her aid. Johanna, too, insisted on being a part of the Dorcas and prided herself on being able to tell the difference between the deserving and the "spongers."

The girls chatted happily as they stuffed stockings full of candies, fruit, and toys for the children. Somehow, they got onto the subject of French lessons.

"Speaking of French reminds me," Elizabeth said with a smile, "of what Mama told me this morning. I'm to be presented on the feast of *Le Petit Noel.*"

"On the Epiphany! How wonderful!" Kate dropped the stocking she was stuffing and embraced her sister. "Sometimes I still wish we could have been twins. Isn't it exciting to think of all the celebrations coming up? First there will be Christmas, then New Year's Eve to usher in the centennial year, then New Year's itself and six days later the Epiphany and your party."

By New Year's Eve, the spirit of the coming festivities had

cast a happy spell over the Drexel household. At lamp-lighting time, Kate and Elizabeth ran from room to room with glowing tapers to be sure that each gas jet was lending its yellow glow to the celebration in observance of 100 years of American freedom.

In front of the first-floor dining room door, Louise, bedecked in five small flags, which she had bought out of her allowance, danced in jubilation. Kate and Elizabeth unwrapped the enormous flag their father had purchased for the celebration, and Hans, the butler, helped them take it upstairs. The Stars and Stripes were then draped gracefully around the balustrade of the balcony overlooking Walnut Street.

"The house must look beautiful!" Elizabeth exclaimed as they ran down the stairs once more.

"And...patriotic!" Kate added with a vehemence that made Elizabeth laugh.

The last meal of 1875 was served early that evening. The girls were anxious to go outside to view their beautifully decorated, illuminated home from the street.

"Perhaps Papa might take us for a walk later," Mrs. Drexel suggested, "and then we could have a look at both Chestnut and Walnut Streets. It should be a sight for all Americans to cherish, not only my three."

The last day of the year had been a busy one for Francis Drexel, but his daughters' pleading expressions made it impossible for him to refuse his wife's request.

Some of the houses in the area were lighted and decorated, but before the Drexels had gone far, they could see that more than a few of their neighbors were either lazy or negligent.

"How could they?" Kate wailed. "At least three-fourths of the houses on Walnut Street are dark. And the mayor ordered that every citizen of Philadelphia should illuminate and drape his house on the evening of December 31! What would George Washington think?"

"If you don't lower your voice," Louise joked, "you'll probably wake up George Washington."

Even Mr. Drexel found it difficult to suppress his amusement when Kate replied, "Wouldn't that be thrilling? Then I wouldn't have to pray for the repose of his soul any more. I would have all of those prayers to give to somebody else."

Mrs. Drexel was glad that Chestnut Street brought about a change of topic. Kate was pleased that nearly all of the Chestnut Street houses and buildings were brilliantly lighted and properly draped with the Stars and Stripes, which were waving in all directions. The store windows, too, were decorated with red, white, and blue, and the street was crowded with people. From the top of the Chestnut Street Theater a huge calcium light shed its glow on the people below and upon the flags of all nations draped across the building. The walls of many of the houses were agleam with Chinese lanterns.

The girls wanted to walk all the way to the historic Old State House, but their father adopted his "enough-is-enough" air, and Mrs. Drexel suggested that it must be past Louise's bedtime.

Kate and her sisters were awakened that night by the boom of cannons, ringing church bells, and hundreds of penny trumpets announcing the death of the old year and the birth of the new. The girls sat up in bed and listened until the last bell had been rang and most of the penny trumpets had fallen silent.

"If only," Kate wished, "we had seven-league boots, we could go down to Independence Hall and watch the hoisting of the United States flag."

"You can go to Independence Hall," Elizabeth mumbled as her head hit the pillow. "I'm going to sleep."

On the morning of January 6, the house was already astir when the girls arose. An extra corps of servants had been hired for the banquet at which Mr. Drexel would present his eldest daughter to society.

Louise loved excitement, and Miss Cassidy, who was slightly inclined to favor her youngest pupil, had trouble getting her to the classroom. Kate had to force herself to keep from laughing at the ridiculous answers Louise gave during class. More than once Miss Cassidy consulted the watch pinned to her shirtwaist, and no one was sad when she announced that they were dismissed.

"Oh, Elizabeth must be too excited for words," Louise cried as she rushed out of the classroom. "I'm going to see how she looks."

On the first floor, men were busy adorning the chandeliers with green smilax vines and pinks. The dining room door was partly open, and Kate was surprised to see the soon-to-be debutante methodically counting the best silver forks and spoons.

"Aren't you excited at all?" Louise asked. "I know my cheeks would be as red as roses if I were going to be presented tonight."

"When the time comes," Elizabeth announced with a slight air of importance, "you will feel differently."

Kate smiled as Louise mimicked her older sister, and Miss Cassidy decided this was a good time to hustle the younger girls off for a late afternoon ride.

When they returned, the house was ready. The sight of swallow-tailed waiters flying around in search of tumblers and plates amused them to no end. Miss Cassidy permitted them to peer in at the dining room table that was elegantly set with large India dishes and handsome gilt candelabra. There were side tables filled with elegant cakes, meringues, jellied chicken,

chicken salad, and more dainty delicacies than the girls could recognize.

At 7:30 P.M., Kate and Louise peeped over the banisters for a look at their parents who stood in the library awaiting the first guest. Johanna had already quarreled with one of the waiters. She joined the girls but refrained from any comment. She was enjoying one of her silent moods.

"They look so funny," Louise decided. "Papa looks gloomy. Mama's dress is pretty—but she doesn't look happy, either. What's wrong with them, Joe?"

For a few seconds Kate thought Joe was going to continue to sulk, but Louise had a way with the temperamental Miss Ryan.

"Well," Joe began, "it's like this. When a young bird learns to fly, and his wings get strong, he soon leaves the nest. Your mother and father know it, and it's eating at their hearts. For sure it's martyrs they look like. *That's* what's wrong with them!"

Joe and Kate exchanged knowing smiles. They were saved from further explanation by the appearance of Miss Cassidy. She suggested in her most gentle voice that there was still time for the girls to run down and say good night to their parents.

Elizabeth, beautiful in her simple white gown and a single strand of pearls at the neck, joined her parents while Kate and Louise were in the library. It was only then that Kate saw her mother and father smile. *Joe was right,* she thought. They were sad because their "birds" were learning to fly.

After the party, a new atmosphere of excitement enveloped the Drexel household. There was a rush of invitations, callers, intimate dinner parties.

The date for moving to Saint Michel's was postponed because May 10 had been set aside as Centennial Day. This was the event the family had looked forward to for so long. The day was to begin with a parade and end with formal centenary ceremonies.

Like most of their neighbors on the square, the Drexels gathered on the upstairs balcony to watch the parade. Walnut Street had finally been roused from the lethargy that had irked Kate so much on New Year's Eve, and now a slight breeze waved the flags, which hung from every residence.

Louise began enthusiastically waving the small flags she held as soon as she heard the first roll of the drums. Leading the impressive procession were the mayor and the members of the city council, all handsome, broad-shouldered men who looked aristocratic as they rode past on prancing horses.

The companies of infantrymen that followed presented a colorful spectacle, some dressed in gray, some in red and blue, and others in blue and white. They were followed by sunburned Marines in blue suits and white hats, and then by a regiment of men wearing yellow knee breeches, black cutaway jackets and three-cornered George Washington hats.

Louise clapped as horses drawing bulky field artillery and the drum and bugle corps filed past. Romantic-looking aides-de-camp galloped the entire length of the parade bringing messages from one general to another.

There must have been a practical joker among the officials in charge, for, at the end of the parade celebrating America's independence from Great Britain, rode a figure representing John Bull. Fat and sneering, he passed by as the last band played the national anthem.

The Drexels were startled when Johanna, standing just inside the balcony with Miss Cassidy, shouted, "*This* is for you," as she waved her fist menacingly and stepped forward so as to be in full view. The crowd shouted and applauded, and Kate thought she saw the sneer on John Bull's face shift briefly to a half smile.

When the parade was over, there were many callers at the Drexel home. Dinner was followed by a mad rush to get Kate dressed before 9:00. She was to join her father's sister, Mrs. Lankenau, and her husband and guests at the centennial ceremonies.

Kate reached the Lankenau residence in time to be presented by her uncle to the German ambassador. She never quite understood the pronunciation of the ambassador's name, but she knew he was a baron. She was also impressed by the manner in which he snatched off the three-cornered hat he was wearing and bowed with stiff formality.

A spring shower had fallen shortly before dusk, and the grounds around the centennial buildings were soggy enough to make walking uncomfortable. The ladies in the Lankenau party held their dresses as high as they dared in an attempt to avoid the mud.

A friend of her uncle's had offered the group the use of his apartment in the main building, and Uncle John was fussing and fuming because the man was not at the appointed place when they arrived. Kate, who walked alongside the uniformed baron, had resigned herself to standing in the mud to see the centennial opening. Uncle John's friend soon appeared, however, and led them up to his quarters.

"And there," Kate later told Miss Cassidy, "were twenty other people to whom he had extended the same invitation—all talking and looking out from the long line of windows into the large square between Memorial Hall and the main building. It was not long, though, before we were comfortably seated.

"To our left," she continued, "we could see a platform

extending from the main building. Almost a thousand men and women were waiting there to sing the centennial chorus. In the meantime, an orchestra played the national air of every country represented by an ambassador. You should have seen the baron when they played *Heil dir im Seigeskranz!*

"As far as the eye could see, there were people pushing and jostling each other. Every inch of ground was covered. Between the main building and Memorial Hall, was a sort of alley, which was set aside as a passageway for the invited guests. A line of soldiers had to press continually against the crowd to keep the people back.

"But the funniest of all," Kate laughed, "was the sight of about twenty people who escaped the mad crush by climbing up onto the two large prancing bronze horses in front of Memorial Hall. It was drizzling, and there they were with open umbrellas sitting on the backs, necks and raised legs of the noble animals.

"We heard a loud clapping and even louder hurrahs. Uncle John's friend announced that the emperor and empress of Brazil were approaching. I got a good look at the empress. She was a little above average in height, middle-aged, with a kind, benevolent face. Dressed in lilac silk gown, she wore something that looked like a white wreath on her head.

"I was still looking at her when thunderous applause broke out, and there was President Grant and the whole diplomatic corps. It was so *American!*" Kate declared. "The band played *The Star Spangled Banner* while everyone stood at attention.

"Then there was utter silence. Bishop Sindey repeated the prayer, which had been composed especially for the Centennial. I just kept thinking that, in spite of the rain, God must have been smiling on the whole ceremony. One hundred years of independence!"

Chapter

The First Cloud

Chapter 5

The First Cloud

The centennial year passed and the Drexels were happy to settle down to a more tranquil pace of life. Relatives and near-relatives had found it convenient to visit anyone within radius of Philadelphia's Fairmount Park during that memorable year, and the Drexel hospitality had attracted numerous visitors, including many priests.

One morning, as the girls were finishing breakfast, there was a great commotion at the back of the house. Several workmen were carrying a huge crate upstairs. The girls were curious to know what was in it, but Elizabeth, who no longer attended Miss Cassidy's classes, had to go to discuss menus with the cook. Kate had to rush to the classroom to study for final examinations. Louise was the only one who had time to investigate. It did her no good, however, since the crate remained tightly nailed.

That afternoon, Mrs. Drexel had the servants open the crate that had been placed in the room Kate shared with Elizabeth. The girls were overjoyed when they recognized a beautiful stained glass window that an English firm had exhibited at the centennial. The central figure was a young girl weaving. An older woman leaned forward as if giving instructions. They were dressed in biblical style, and the Drexels decided that the artist had been inspired by the visit of the

59

Virgin Mary to Saint Elizabeth. The window was named "Saint Elizabeth" and installed in the girls' bedroom.

Wise Mrs. Drexel had intended for her daughters to be impressed by this lovely model of feminine industry, and she soon called the girls together for a conference.

When their mother began to discuss a division of household duties, the girls thought she was joking or leading up to some pleasant change in routine.

"What is there for us to do?" Louise asked, after she realized her mother was serious. "There are so many servants here and at Saint Michel's."

"And what will the servants think when we come snooping around?" Elizabeth asked.

"Kate, have you no questions or objections?" Mrs. Drexel asked patiently.

"I remember," Kate replied, smiling, "the music lessons we didn't want to practice and the many times when we objected to spending extra hours in the classroom with Mademoiselle de Saint Marsault. But when we were in Europe, especially the day in Vienna when I was looking for an English confessor, we understood why you had insisted that we have lessons in French. So..."

"So, dear Mama," Elizabeth, who seemed to grow closer to her mother each year, interrupted, "we know you must have some good reason in mind. We're ready to do whatever you ask."

Kate knew that her mother was pleased as she went on to make assignments for each girl. Louise, who loved the outdoors, was given the responsibility of the farm and garden when they were at Saint Michel's. During their stay in the city, she was to be concerned with the outside appearance of the house and of the yard.

"You spend most of your waking moments outdoors anyway," her mother reminded. "And you, Elizabeth, would rather ride and eat than anything else. So you will supervise the kitchen as well as the stables."

Kate, who was more inclined than her sisters to enjoy pulling loose threads together, was appointed housekeeper. Hers was the task of attending to all of the details connected with the interior of the house. She was to oversee the butler, maids, seamstress, laundress, coachman, and any servants brought in for special occasions. The girls had to make weekly reports and, though she accepted recommendations, their mother reserved the right to make final decisions when emergencies arose. The girls enjoyed being helpful, and Mrs. Drexel was delighted with the way they discharged their duties. She was happy, too, in the knowledge that she was preparing them for the day when they would be presiding over their own homes.

Kate passed Miss Cassidy's final examinations, and school days ended for her on July 2, 1878. She was formally introduced to society in January 1879, when she was twenty. Her debut followed much the same pattern as the earlier party given for Elizabeth. It was comforting to Kate to have Elizabeth with her at the coming-out party, and most of the invitations that came to the Walnut Street home thereafter were addressed to the "Misses Drexel." Kate admitted that she was secretly glad when the first season was over and they left the city for Saint Michel's where the months always seemed to pass much too quickly.

"Each year," she laughingly told her sisters, "just when I

think the boys and girls in the Sunday school class are ready to sprout wings, it's time to close. Never," she insisted, "are they the same when we come back to Saint Michel's for Christmas."

Kate loved the old farmhouse and always felt a pang when moving day arrived.

"As much as I hate leaving Saint Michel's," she remarked the day the family was returning to the city for her second social season, "this is the only time we're all together when we drive over the pike and pass so many familiar sights."

"But the horses seem so slow today," her mother commented, "and we hardly have time for extended sight-seeing. I hope we won't keep your father waiting for dinner."

"Mama," Elizabeth began as she leaned over to brush her mother's cheek with a kiss, "you always say the same thing. Yet Papa is always playing the organ when we get home, and we have plenty of time to wash and dress before the music stops and he realizes we're in the house."

Mrs. Drexel had to laugh with her girls. Miss Cassidy and Joe, who were waiting at 1503, commented on their flushed cheeks when they arrived.

"It's proud I am to see a little color in your mother's cheeks," Joe confided to the girls while they were dressing. "I haven't liked the looks of her for a long time. She's much too pale and thin to suit me."

"It couldn't be the strain of worrying over one Johanna Ryan, could it?" Elizabeth laughed away the idea of her mother's not looking well.

"Joe's forever making gloomy observations." Louise was annoyed. "Mama always looks beautiful!"

"I want you to know one thing." Kate spoke seriously, though her sisters had spoken with humor. "If anything ever happened to Mama, I would enter the convent."

"I guess you're satisfied," Elizabeth told Joe. "You've just driven my sister into the cloister!"

"Praise be!" Joe cried. "The organ has stopped and your father will be going down to dinner any minute. Hurry, or we'll all catch it."

Johanna decided not to mention Kate's comment to Mrs. Drexel because she couldn't very well explain how the conversation had come up. She did, however, speak of it to Bishop James O'Connor. Kate corresponded regularly with His Excellency, who had been the pastor of the church the Drexels attended when at Saint Michel's. He later became the first bishop of Omaha, Nebraska. Joe told him what Kate had said the next time he came to Saint Michel's to celebrate Mass.

The bishop knew that Francis and Emma Drexel had instilled in each of the girls a deep sense of responsibility for their neighbor. He also believed that, of the three, Kate felt this responsibility most keenly. He prayed that God would grant him the wisdom to counsel Kate well when the proper time came.

Mrs. Drexel was pleased that so many of their friends invited Kate and Elizabeth for visits. The two girls were often the center of attention at house parties in Long Branch, Asbury Park, and other fashionable gathering places. Their father usually joined the girls to accompany them home, and their Uncle Michel, whom they secretly called "The Prince," often served as their escort.

There was a constant exchange of letters between the girls and their mother, and she was delighted that they met so many young women of their own age. She was concerned, though, that they seldom mentioned young men in a serious way. When she spoke of it to her husband, he replied quickly, and with a touch of annoyance, "There's plenty of time for that, Emma."

Kate and Elizabeth were visiting relatives at the seashore during the summer of 1880 when Mrs. Drexel had a dream about her second daughter that seemed so real, she awoke calling Kate's name.

"What's wrong, dear?" her husband gently prodded. "You know the girls are at Long Branch."

"It was a dream, Francis," Mrs. Drexel answered in a stunned tone of voice. "So—beautiful—yet so strange."

"The way you were calling for Kate, I wasn't sure *what* was happening." Mr. Drexel chuckled.

"But don't you want to hear about it?"

"The dream? Why, Emma, no one pays any attention to those..."

"But this one was different," Mrs. Drexel broke in. "I saw the painting of a door, and it was so beautiful! It was the kind of door we often saw in Europe in the walls of church sanctuaries—the kind that led to a reliquary. The one I dreamed about was bedecked with many rare and dazzling jewels, but it was locked. I was curious to open it and learn what relics were kept there. That's where Kate came in."

Mrs. Drexel was so serious that her husband began to listen intently. "Kate and Elizabeth were with me," she continued. "I asked Kate for the key and her face was almost as radiant as the jewels when she said, 'Jesus holds the key, for this is the door of his heart. He opens only to those who knock and ask.' It was so real...just as if she were right here in the room, Francis."

"Then why were you calling her name so desperately?"

"Because of what happened after Kate spoke. Elizabeth laughed at her pious interpretation and said it was nonsense. Poor Kate looked so hurt I thought she would cry. But when I tried to console her, the picture started fading and I remember calling out to Kate. I only wish I understood its meaning. Sometimes I think our Lord is trying to tell me something."

"About what?"

"About Kate."

Mr. Drexel put an arm around his wife. "Now Emma, the trouble is that Kate is a middle child and we don't know what to do about her. As much as I hate to admit it, we both know that Elizabeth will probably marry one of those boys who always seem to be calling lately—the Smith boy, or one of the others. Louise will do whatever she decides—whether it be to head Drexel & Sons, or marry. But we're not sure about Kate, and that's what's worrying you. We shall just have to wait until Kate makes up her mind. And rest assured, my dear, that once Katie Drexel makes up her mind about her life's work you will probably be the first to know. Don't rush her. There's plenty of time. For now, let's go back to sleep."

But Emma couldn't go back to sleep. *I only wish I, too, believed there was plenty of time,* she thought. *He's so right, though. Elizabeth will marry, and Louise will never be lonely regardless of what she decides to do. I must pray that God may help me to understand what he wants of Kate.*

By the fall of 1881, it was apparent that Johanna had not been far wrong in saying that Mrs. Drexel didn't look well. Even Elizabeth and Louise had to admit that their mother's health seemed to be failing. In the end, she was found to be suffering from cancer. All three of the girls tried to relieve her of household duties and cares, but it was Kate who appeared with a glass of water when her mother felt suddenly thirsty, or placed a dish of fruit on the table closest to her bed on evenings when Mrs. Drexel had scarcely touched her dinner. Kate would be her mother's nurse during her long illness.

Mr. Drexel called in the best doctors available and, by the spring of the following year, his wife seemed better. The family returned to Saint Michel's where they stayed through the fall and into the early winter. Mrs. Drexel was beginning to take an interest in household affairs again. In December, she surprised the family by deciding that they would not spend Christmas in the country.

"It's been so long," she said dreamily, "since we passed a Christmas on Walnut Street. Joe and Miss Cassidy can go in early and make sure the house is ready. We will follow in the carriage, and when we get there, the house will be all aglow with lights. The wreaths at the windows will add a holiday touch, and your father will be at the organ. I do hope he'll play some Christmas music for me."

The family arrived back in Philadelphia five days before Christmas. Mrs. Drexel's every wish had been granted and, as she smiled on them, her husband and her children told themselves that this was one of many happy Christmases to come.

Their joy continued to mount when, near the end of January, she went for a drive through the city she loved so much. This happiness was short-lived however, for less than a week later Emma Bouvier Drexel died. A Requiem Mass was offered at Saint Mary's, and she was laid to rest in the Bouvier vault in Saint Mary's churchyard.

Louise and Elizabeth seemed to cling to each other in their sorrow, but Kate sat with her father through the first weeks. Together they read the obituaries from papers published all over the country. Though Kate knew about most of her mother's charities, she was amazed to learn that more than 150 poor families depended upon Emma Drexel to pay their rent. It was estimated, she read, that this "Lady Bountiful" distributed over $20,000 each year among the needy of her native Philadelphia.

Despite their sorrow it was soon apparent to everyone that Mrs. Drexel's death had wrought a remarkable change in Elizabeth. Almost overnight, she seemed to step into her mother's place, and the comfort of each member of the family became her chief concern. All social activities were pushed aside and, as soon as possible, Elizabeth moved the family back to Saint Michel's in order to avoid the surroundings so closely connected with the death of their beloved mother.

As the flowers blossomed on the grounds of Saint Michel's, there was gradually heard again the happy laughter, which had once signaled that the Drexels were at home. Louise spent most of her days outdoors with her dog or riding with Kate and Elizabeth. Mr. Drexel spent his days at the bank, but faced an empty place at the end of the table when he sat down to dinner with the girls. By the end of the summer, he decided that a trip to Europe would dull the edge of their grief. Little did Mr. Drexel realize how this trip would alter Kate's life.

Chapter 6

A Vision

Kate and her sisters were grateful for the warm affection with which Johanna and Miss Cassidy surrounded them after their mother's death. Since Johanna had gone on the first European trip, Mr. Drexel spoke about taking Miss Cassidy on the second excursion. Louise and Elizabeth were delighted at this prospect, but Kate, for some reason, showed little enthusiasm.

"You don't seem a bit happy that Miss Cassidy is going," Elizabeth remarked one day. "Don't you think that she deserves to? She's always the one who's left behind."

"It's not that—I'm not sure Mama would have placed so much responsibility on Joe," Kate replied thoughtfully, "though I'm sure she would have wanted Miss Cassidy to have the trip. Joe has the best heart in the world, but we all know that there are times when she can be very highhanded with the servants. You know how Mama felt about that, and we must try to carry out her wishes."

"Leave it to you to see the practical side of the matter," Elizabeth sighed. "I guess we were thinking more of our own pleasure. It's true…if Joe should happen to fling one of her temperamental fits…"

"We just might come home to two houses and a farm—minus any servants except for one Johanna Ryan," Louise agreed.

"Oh, it might not be that bad," Kate laughed.

"Kate's right," Elizabeth said. "I'll ask Papa to book passage for Joe and to ask Miss Cassidy if she will consent to act as a sort of general manager of home affairs. How does that sound?"

The Drexels sailed on the S. S. *Scythia* in early October of 1883. Mr. Drexel and Joe were the only able-bodied sailors among them for the first two days, but after Joe and the cabin boy forced the girls to drink the juice of two lemons, Kate and Louise rallied enough to take part in shipboard activities.

"We went around recommending lemon juice to the bilious-faced passengers stretched out on steamer chairs," Kate wrote, "and had the satisfaction of putting two patients on their legs—but Elizabeth was not of that number."

The other passengers recognized the Drexels and, having read of their recent sorrow, made special efforts to be friendly.

Kate, now twenty-five, knew that Miss Cassidy and Joe had shared her mother's concern over her lack of interest in suitors, so she made sure that her letters to Miss Cassidy contained a description of all the young men she met aboard the *Scythia*. *Yet there are times,* Kate thought as she finished one of those letters, *when I think she knows—almost better than anyone except Mama and Father O'Connor—that I could never find happiness in a life devoted to social pleasure.*

When they landed in England, Kate and her sisters reminded their father not to chance another visit to Westminster Abbey with Johanna. After a short trip to Chester, they went on to Dover and from there to Brussels, Antwerp, Amsterdam, and The Hague. Then came Nuremberg, Munich, and Venice.

Although each of the girls thought of their mother constantly, Kate seemed to find it easiest to speak of her with her father. Mr. Drexel had also noticed that it was Kate who arranged for memorial Masses to be celebrated whenever they revisited churches they had first seen with their mother. It was also Kate who directed Miss Cassidy to send Aunt Louise a ten-dollar check each month as a Mass offering.

Often, when the girls went to an early Mass in Venice, they came out of the church to find their father feeding the pigeons on the piazza of Saint Mark's. One morning, after Louise and Elizabeth walked toward the hotel, Kate remained with her father. He spoke of love for animals—dogs, horses, and the "little feathered things."

"Saint Francis loved them, too," Kate murmured, half to herself.

"But it is for his love of the poor that you admire the saint of Assisi, isn't it, Kate?" her father asked quietly.

"That came later," she admitted. "It was Francis, the carefree troubadour, who interested us all when we were children and Mama used to read to us about him."

"Your mother had a dream about you not too long before..."

"...She wrote us about it," Kate broke in, wincing at the sadness in her father's voice. "She said it was such a beautiful dream and so real."

"Yes. But I blame myself for not having paid more attention to what she said that night."

"Why, Papa?"

"I think she knew she was going to die. And she was worried about you."

"But she told us she was worried because she couldn't understand the dream and because Elizabeth had laughed at my interpretation," Kate remembered. "Why was she worried about me, Papa?"

"I'm not sure." Mr. Drexel placed a hand on his daughter's arm. "Perhaps you will understand that better than your father.

Let's go into church and ask her to intercede for us so that we may become resigned to this separation and that you may understand whatever divine Providence wills you to do."

Kate knelt in a pew facing the Madonna of San Marco. She thought of the dream her father had mentioned. *If only I could talk to Mama now*, she thought. *There is something I must do— but I'm not sure what it is.*

Suddenly the sun burst through the clouds, which had overshadowed the early hours of the day, and found its way to the window nearest the painting. The light that played around the face of the Madonna was almost blinding. Then it softened, and the face Kate saw seemed to be the face of her mother.

Kate turned toward her father, his head bowed in reverent prayer, but the Madonna frowned and Kate stayed the hand she had raised. Instead, she rose quietly and walked quickly to the foot of the painting. Once more, the face wore a smile and the lips parted as if waiting to speak.

"What is it you want to tell me?" Kate whispered.

"Freely have you received; freely give," said a voice which was so soft Kate strained to hear each word.

"Mother, that's the Gospel passage on which Francis based his Rule," Kate gasped. Then the image was dark again—except for the reflection from the candles—and the face of the Madonna was as it had been when Kate first entered the church.

She looked around to be sure she wasn't dreaming. An altar boy came out of the sacristy with a lighted taper and walked toward the main altar. Mass was about to begin, and Kate returned to her father.

Before she could collect her thoughts, a hand was in front of her. It held out a picture of the little Madonna before whom she had just knelt. Kate looked up into the face of an attendant. The man impatiently pushed the card at her, handed one to Mr. Drexel, and continued to pass them out to the faithful gathering for this late Mass.

All during Mass Kate kept remembering the words, "Freely have you received; freely give." She wanted so much to tell her father about it, but she remembered the frown on the Madonna's face when she had raised her hand to touch him. Later, after they returned to the hotel, she was tempted to talk to Elizabeth about the vision—for Kate was certain that that was what it had been. But each time she felt so inclined, she remembered her mother's dream and Elizabeth's interpretation of her description as nonsense. That night, when her father handed Kate a letter from Bishop O'Connor, she suddenly realized that this experience could be discussed only with her spiritual director.

It was late that night when Kate finished her letter to the bishop. Then she wrote the date—November 18, 1883—on the holy card of the Madonna at whose feet she had received a part of Saint Francis' Rule. She vowed that this Rule would become her way of life, too.

I'll keep this forever, she thought, placing the picture in her missal. *The only trouble is that I still don't know how I am to give of what I have. If I am just to continue with the Dorcas, Mama would have said so. Surely they—my mother and the Lord's—will help me to find the way.*

The Drexels next made a pilgrimage to Padua where they begged the intercession of Saint Anthony on behalf of Aunt Elizabeth, Mr. Drexel's sister, who was then seriously ill. They reached Rome in time to celebrate Christmas.

On Christmas Eve the family attended Mass in the sacristy of Santa Maria Maggiore, where five boards said to be from the manger in which the infant Jesus had lain the first Christmas in Bethlehem were exposed for veneration. Kate felt very close to our Lady and her Son in the presence of this relic. In an effort to be patient in regard to her future work, she reminded herself of the years Jesus was subject to his parents' will.

Soon after they had arrived in Rome, the Drexels met two priests. The acquaintance seemed only casual then, but these two men were destined to greatly influence the lives of the Drexel sisters. One was the Most Reverend John Seghers, bishop of Vancouver Island, known as the "Apostle of Alaska." The other was Father Hylebos, a Belgian priest who had taken up missionary work in the northwestern part of the United States.

In the meetings that followed, Bishop Seghers told many interesting stories of his work among the Eskimos, but Kate was most enchanted by Father Hylebos' accounts of his travels over American Indian Territory. The priests and the Drexels parted with little thought of ever meeting again.

A few days after Christmas, the Drexels received permission to be present at a private Mass celebrated by the Holy Father. Joe, whose health had prevented her from taking part in many of the trip's activities, solemnly promised to control herself if she were allowed to go. The family was received by Pope Leo XIII after the Mass, and the Pontiff bestowed his blessing upon the faithful Philadelphians and sent one to their friends and relatives in America.

As Kate knelt at the feet of the Pope, she raised her head and looked into his eyes. The kindness she saw there gave her courage and a great feeling of peace rushed over her.

Somehow, she thought, *I feel he has the key that will unlock the door for me. I must find a way to meet him again—I must. I must!*

The memory of the pope's gaze so absorbed Kate, she barely heard her father saying, as they were all packing to leave Rome, that he had a surprise for Kate. Only after he mentioned a visit to Sienna, did Kate come out of her thoughts. At last, she was going to visit the home of her patron saint!

It was a frosty morning when the family reached Sienna and walked down Dyers Street to the house where Saint Catherine had lived. Inside, they stood before an altar that had been built over the chimney in the kitchen.

"I almost feel as if Saint Catherine could come into this room right now, push the chimney aside, and start cooking," Elizabeth murmured.

"I'd much prefer a fire that would give out some heat," Louise whispered back, shivering.

Kate wandered into Catherine's tiny bedroom. Everything was unchanged. The smell of ill-tanned leather lingered still, and Kate remembered that Catherine had been the child of a prosperous wool dyer. While the rest of the family visited the little chapel, which had been built over a part of the house and garden, Kate remained behind in the cell-like bedroom.

"Please, dear Catherine," she whispered as she knelt on the spot where the saint had once slept on her bed of boards, "beg our divine Lord to give me the spiritual enlightenment to give freely so that those with whom I share shall proclaim his greater honor and glory."

The Drexels traveled on, and the first anniversary of Mrs. Drexel's death was only a day or so away when they reached San Remo. They had intended to have her anniversary Mass celebrated at Lourdes, but with the anniversary so near, they remained in San Remo to commemorate the day.

It was February 1, when Joe, the girls, and their father arrived in Lourdes. During those next four hard-on-the-knees days when they prayed at the grotto, drank the water, kissed the ground, lit the candles, and bathed in the water of the miraculous spring, the girls felt completely awed by the spiritual atmosphere of Lourdes.

"It's like being in another world," Kate mused. "The Hotel de la Grotte might just as well be on another planet."

The Drexels reached Paris during the season of Lent and, by Easter, they were in London. Johanna's grief over the loss of Mrs. Drexel was still strong, and the girls began to realize that the trip had been too strenuous for her. They were all glad to sail for home at the end of April.

Soon after reaching the States, Aunt Elizabeth died—an added sorrow for the entire family. They dreaded going back to Saint Michel's, though they were glad to be in familiar surroundings again. They watched their father intently as he walked from room to room on their first night home.

"He seems to expect to find Mama hiding in some corner," Kate remarked to her sisters.

In an effort to create a cheerful atmosphere, Miss Cassidy had flowers placed throughout the house, but even this reminded the family of their beloved mother who had planted most of them.

In spite of her protracted mourning, it was "good old Joe" who made the girls push aside their own grief. "Mr. Drexel isn't looking his usual self," she told them one evening as they sat on the porch awaiting their father's return from the city. "Ever since we've been back he's been restless. He isn't eating well, either."

"That might be my fault," Elizabeth spoke up. "I haven't been spending as much time on the weekly menu as I should. But I'll try to do better and see if I can remember some of Mama's favorite dishes."

"I'll have to start going on walks with Papa again," Louise decided. "I guess we were so busy thinking of ourselves, we forgot how lonely it's been for Papa."

Kate thought a moment before she spoke. "I'll have him set up a housekeeping account for me," she said. "Then I can relieve him of taking care of some of the bills."

"Well, at least I didn't get my head bit off as I expected," Joe snorted as she rose and walked toward the door. "A body never knows what to say these days."

"We're really very grateful to you, Joe," Kate replied, smiling, "for pointing out to us just how blind we've been."

"It's been hard on me, too." Joe stood in the doorway with her back to Kate and her sisters. "She was just like a sister to me." With a cry, Louise ran to the older woman who, by that time, was sobbing openly.

In the distance, Kate heard the crunch of carriage wheels on the driveway.

"Take them upstairs," she told her older sister while shooing them toward the door. "It will never do for Papa to see both of them crying. This is just the kind of scene that will make him feel worse."

Kate breathed a sigh of relief when her father greeted her. He was so cheerful it made her curious.

"I have good news tonight," he said smiling broadly and looking around. "Where's the rest of the family?"

"They're late dressing for dinner. But they'll be down by the time you're ready," Kate quickly assured him.

Mr. Drexel chuckled as his daughters plied him with questions about his good news. "No," he teased, "it might spoil your dinner. Better wait till after dessert."

It wasn't until after the table had been cleared that Mr. Drexel finally revealed his secret. "We're going out West—all the way to Portland, Oregon. And we'll make a special detour so we can see Yellowstone Park."

"Will we be going through Indian Territory?" Kate eagerly questioned. "Remember the stories Father Hylebos told us in Rome about his work among the Indians?"

"We certainly will pass through Indian Territory," Mr. Drexel assured. "But, I'm not yet convinced that three city-bred girls will really enjoy such a trip?"

"We certainly will!" exclaimed Louise while her eyes were dancing. "And I'm going to get the best Indian pony I can find and ride all over the mountains."

"You won't have to worry about the mountains," her father laughed. "We'll be traveling in a special railroad car, the *Yellowstone*. It belongs to J. J. Hill, president of the Northern Pacific Railroad—and he's putting it at our disposal for the duration of the trip."

"I still want a pony," Louise insisted. "All my life I've wanted an Indian pony."

"And all my life I've wanted to see a real Indian village," Kate admitted quietly.

Chapter 7

Escape and Adventures

It was September 8, 1884—our Lady's birthday—when Kate and her sisters set out from Saint Michel's on the most thrilling trip of their lives. After Mass and Holy Communion at Eden Hall, the girls and their father drove into the city. They were joined by their cousin Mary Dixon, the daughter of Aunt Elizabeth whose recent death had so grieved them, and two young men from the Drexel firm. The richly furnished *Yellowstone* stood on a sidetrack waiting for the Drexels and for the engine which would start them on their journey westward.

Kate's intense interest in Father Hylebos' Indian missions had not escaped her father. *Perhaps,* he thought, *this is a key to the vocation she's seeking.* When Drexel & Company began to consider investing in the Northern Pacific Railroad, Francis Drexel knew he would have to make a trip West, which he hoped would serve a practical as well as a pleasant purpose.

As the train sped westward, Mr. Drexel crossed off the days of the week. Gardiner, Montana, was to be the first stop. The conductor had assured Mr. Drexel they would reach that town on Saturday night so that they could attend Mass on Sunday morning. One of the railroad officials had arranged to meet them there.

The *Yellowstone* was sidetracked, however, and missed connections. When Mr. Drexel learned that they might not reach Gardiner before Sunday afternoon, he demanded that the *Yellowstone* be stopped at Bismarck, North Dakota. A telegram was sent to Gardiner, advising J. J. Hill's agent of the change.

The Drexel party attended an early Mass at Bismarck. When they returned to the train, they were told that it would be several hours before the engine that would take them on to Gardiner would pick up the car. The girls wanted to stretch their legs, so back to church they went.

"I had so hoped," Kate told her father later, "that the sermon would bring some consolation to Mary. Her sorrow over losing dear Aunt Elizabeth seems to hang over all of us whenever there's a lull. Instead, we get a homily on 'The Neglect of Parents in Educating Boys'—a very unlikely subject for four young unmarried ladies!"

The delay stretched into the night. The *Yellowstone* was switched around until it was on the main track and an engine finally picked it up. The party returned for the night, knowing that the *Yellowstone* would be approaching Gardiner, Montana, when they awakened.

Early the next morning the girls found their father anxiously consulting his watch as they joined him and the young men from his office.

"We're pulling into Gardiner now," he explained, "but we're twelve hours late. I was to meet one of J. J. Hill's men here—that's why I sent the telegram. But I mentioned only a six-hour delay."

When the conductor informed them that they would be in Gardiner in five minutes, the girls gathered on the observation platform at the rear of the car.

As the train pulled into the station, they noticed an unusually large crowd of people standing around. "What's all the excitement?" the girls heard the conductor call to one of the trackmen.

"Ain't sure yet," the man answered, "but it looks as if the bandits are riding again."

"I think we'd better go inside," Kate suggested.

Before the family could leave the *Yellowstone*, an excited young man came aboard. He was so busy mopping his red face that he collided with Mr. Drexel in the doorway. "Are you Mr. Francis A. Drexel?" he asked anxiously.

"I am." Mr. Drexel bowed. "And who, may I ask, are you?"

"Mr. Drexel, I've never been happier to see anyone in my life!" the young man sighed. "Mr. Hill instructed me to meet you at the station. I got your telegram Saturday, but it said you would be here last night and that you would wire later—but I never heard another thing—and then, after all the excitement…"

"Pardon me," Mr. Drexel interrupted, "but what *is* all the excitement about?"

"Oh—you don't know? It seems that word got around that a party of rich bankers from the East was coming to town, and some outlaws who have been hiding out near here came into town. Somehow, they knew your train was due last night. About thirty minutes before you were expected, they came to the station and pulled their guns on the stationmaster. He thought it was a holdup and tried to fight them…"

"But I sent another telegram saying we'd been delayed still more," interrupted Mr. Drexel again.

"That I never got. You see, Mr. Drexel, the stationmaster is also our telegraph clerk, and he's still in bad shape—much worse than myself." Then, removing his hat, the speaker revealed the large lump on his forehead.

"What happened?" Mr. Drexel gasped in alarm.

"Well, when I came down to meet you, I went to the desk to check if you had left any message. The bandits jumped me as soon as I stepped inside the door. They had already bound and gagged the stationmaster and when I struggled to get away, someone hit me over the head. I don't remember anything else—but a brakeman found both of us gagged and tied when he came on duty this morning."

Mr. Drexel, pale with the thought of what could have happened, turned to his daughters. "If we hadn't stopped to go to Mass in Bismarck we might all be dead. Worse still, those thieves might have held you girls for ransom."

After the narrow escape at Gardiner, the Drexels went on through Idaho and into Washington Territory. They stopped at Tacoma, then only a struggling village.

Kate thought often of the little Madonna of San Marco and of her experience at the feet of the painting. She had been disappointed in Bishop O'Connor's reaction to her letter. He had insisted that she was not ready to begin her life's work, whatever it was to be. Everything that had or was happening, he said, was preparation. Kate was reminded of this by a pleasant surprise in Tacoma.

When she had asked where they might find a Catholic church, the maid in the hotel had pointed to a tiny building perched on one of the hills. With their cousin, Mary, the girls climbed the hill early the following morning. They stopped at the modest rectory next to the church to inquire when the next Mass would be celebrated.

Kate knocked on the door while the others stood on the hillside to admire the scenery. When the door opened, she stood there stunned. Staring at the priest in front of her, she thought, *this can't be the priest we met in Rome. Of all the missions in the Northwest, this couldn't possibly be Father Hylebos' church!*

But it was! And Father Hylebos' greeting banished any doubt.

"To what do I owe the pleasure of having Miss Drexel of Philadelphia call on me?" he laughed heartily. "Or, I should say Misses Drexel," he added as the other girls joined them.

"Kate," Elizabeth demanded after the excitement had died down, "are you sure you didn't know Father Hylebos was here? Maybe this is where you planned all along to see the Indian village."

They all laughed, and Kate insisted she had *no* idea that Father Hylebos was in Tacoma.

Kate's father had made plans for that day, and the *Yellowstone* was scheduled to leave the following afternoon, but it was agreed that the girls would attend an early Mass at Father Hylebos' church the next morning.

"Then I'll drive you out into the forest to see one of my missions—that is, if the mission hasn't moved," he added.

"What do you mean, Father?" Kate asked.

"The Indians move their villages according to the work they're doing," he explained. "We'll go out to Puyallup and, as they say in Philadelphia, hope for luck."

Luck was not with the Philadelphians, however, and when they reached what had been a Native American village, it looked like a deserted meadow to Kate and her sisters.

As they turned away, Father Hylebos saw an old Indian man with a small boy resting by the roadside. "Where?" the priest asked, pointing to the deserted village.

"Hops...hop fields," the old man replied.

"Are you going, too?" Father asked.

"Yes!" The old man grunted and bowed his head several times before he pulled the child to his feet and walked in the direction of the hop fields to which he had pointed.

"They're harvesting the hops," the priest explained. "They will camp as near to the fields as possible. It would be, perhaps, a two-hour drive with these weary old horses pulling us and the carriage."

"Father," Elizabeth asked, "do you mean that old man is going to walk the distance it would take the horses two hours to cover?"

"And what about the little boy?" Kate added. "Perhaps we could make room for them in the carriage."

"He wouldn't accept a ride even if we offered," the priest answered shaking his head. "I don't know whether he was left behind or returned to retrieve some forgotten object. But he will be joining his people, and the child—perhaps his grandson—will be proud to walk along with his grandfather."

The girls agreed that there was not time enough to risk driving deeper into the forest, so they returned to the rectory. When she visited the church, Kate had noticed how bare it appeared and wondered how she could help without offending the priest. When Father Hylebos left them alone, the girls held a conference, each expressing a desire to help. Mr. Drexel had recently opened bank accounts for each of his daughters and left them free to spend their generous monthly allowances as they wished.

"If you don't mind," Kate told her sisters, "I'd like to take Father Hylebos' work as my special charity—like Mama's Dorcas. I've always been interested in Indians. They've had to suffer so many injustices. This way I'll feel that I'm sharing what I have with them."

When Kate spoke to Father Hylebos he was delighted with her offer of help. "I remember your devotion to our Lady," he said, "and we don't yet have a statue. That would be a most welcome gift. The Indians have great love for the mother of our Lord."

Kate selected a statue from a catalogue Father Hylebos gave her, but she hesitated a moment before she wrote the check. She thought of the little Madonna in Venice and the words, "Freely have you received; freely give." The statue would cost $100.00, a large sum back then, and Kate was afraid her father would think her purchase extravagant. Then she remembered Saint Francis and how he had incurred his father's wrath in order to "freely give." Kate Drexel wrote her first check with conviction and joy and thrilled to the sincerity of Father Hylebos' "God bless you, my child!"

That evening, after the *Yellowstone* headed off for Kalama, where they would board a boat to Portland, Kate told her father about the statue.

"I was afraid you would think me extravagant," she admitted.

"My dear Kate," he said, placing his arm around her shoulders with tender affection and feeling, "I'm *glad* you did this."

That night Kate slept peacefully. She dreamed that she was once more talking about the statue with her father and, as he expressed approval, her mother joined them, smiling as she said, "This is the beginning." Even in her sleep Kate seemed to know she was dreaming, but the slumber that followed was deep and refreshing. When they reached Kalama the next day, she felt as if life—a glorious life—were just beginning.

As the Portland-bound boat pulled away from the shore, Kate's sisters and her cousin Mary commented on her high spirits and flushed cheeks.

Mr. Drexel was standing beside his daughter as she leaned against the rail of the deck. "It's our secret Kate, isn't it?" he asked.

"Secret?" Kate looked up at him puzzled. "I'm not sure I understand what you mean, Papa."

"The spirit of giving, Kate. And the happiness it gives you. I hope God always grants you the wisdom to use what you have as well as you did in Tacoma."

A gathering mist dampened the deck and the rest of the party went indoors. Kate and her father remained where they were, watching the land slide away, each filled with an abiding love of God, family, and the vast country they were exploring.

Chapter 8

A Door Is Closed

Miss Cassidy was delighted with the account the three Drexel girls gave of their trip west. On the rare occasions when she exchanged confidences with Johanna, she was apt to refer to the pleasant lines along which her life had fallen. Since the death of her mother, she had lived with the Drexels.

"Few teachers," she said, "have had the opportunity of seeing their pupils develop day by day—then year by year—as has been my lot. Sometimes when I go to the old classroom—now a classroom no longer—it's hard for me to realize that they are grown. Just think of it, my petite Louise is twenty-two years old!"

"Elizabeth is thirty, and it's twenty-seven that Kate will be in November," Johanna reminded. "It's high time Elizabeth and Louise were thinking about families of their own, though I don't think Kate will ever leave her father—not unless something happens to convince her that her life's work is elsewhere."

"You know our Kate," Miss Cassidy smiled. "She was never one to jump at quick decisions, but once she has arrived at a conclusion, she can't be easily swayed. I know her well enough to see that there is something—some course of action—she is weighing now. I've noticed it ever since her mother's death."

Johanna tiptoed to the door and closed it. "I've an idea," she whispered, "that Kate's just waiting for Bishop O'Connor. I don't think it will be so long now before we know what she's going to do."

"I'm not too sure it's only Bishop O'Connor's blessing she is waiting on." Kate's teacher thought for a while. "There's some indecision—I don't know what—but it's there. I do know she isn't interested in any of the young men who come here, though I can't say the same for Elizabeth and Louise."

"Kate seems taken with the idea of helping that priest we met in Rome who works with the Indians out West." Johanna shook her head. "What with the robbers and bad food, I'd be just as happy if she forgot about the good father and his Indians."

Miss Cassidy laughed. "Kate is not one to change easily. She's started corresponding with him already, and I can tell from the letter she showed me that she plans to set aside a portion of her allowance for his missions."

Miss Cassidy was right. Kate had decided to set aside a part of her money for the Indian missions. She shared Father Hylebos' dream that one day there would be a school at Tacoma where children from the Yakima, Tulipup, Puyallup, and Nesqually tribes might be taught reading, writing, and religion.

As Christmas approached, Kate and her sisters busied themselves with preparations for giving gifts of food, clothing, and money through the Dorcas.

"Do you think this is the way Mama would have done it?" was a question they often asked each other when checking over the list of families who were to receive help and deciding on what form this help should take.

A few days before Christmas the girls received a partial answer to their question. Johanna, who had always assisted Mrs. Drexel with the Dorcas, inspected the work the girls had done with a critical eye.

"Your own dear mother could not have done better," she said approvingly, "though she might have saved a penny more here and there. You'll learn, though."

The sisters laughed when Johanna left the room because it was a standing joke that their friend was wary of paying compliments.

It was a quiet family Christmas, and on January 29, the girls and their father attended a second anniversary Mass for Mrs. Drexel. As she approached Communion, Kate thought about the little Virgin of San Marco and was pleased that her father was kneeling beside her when she begged her two mothers to smile upon their child.

Two days after the anniversary, Mr. Drexel told his daughters he wanted to go to Saint Michel's. The weather was cold, but clear, and the sisters enjoyed the ride to Torresdale. Their father was exceptionally quiet as they reminisced and pointed out familiar places. Occasionally he smiled at some happy memory, but later they commented on how pensive he had been throughout the journey.

After lunch, Louise, who was her father's favorite walking companion, coaxed him into making a short tour of the grounds. Kate insisted that he wear a muffler, and personally buttoned his greatcoat at the neck. When Elizabeth made as if to help her father with his gloves, he pushed her aside playfully.

"Anybody would think I was an invalid," he laughed, "to see you girls fussing over me."

"I'd rather believe," Kate said with feeling, "that they would think you were a *very* special father."

A slight drizzle had begun to fall before Mr. Drexel and Louise returned, but they changed their clothes immediately. When they rejoined Elizabeth and Kate, they brought them up to date on the barnyard happenings.

The next day—Sunday, February 1, 1885—the family returned to the city. Dinner was served in the early afternoon,
and Louise and her father decided they would finish the walk,
which had been interrupted by the rain the day before. The
next morning Mr. Drexel appeared to have a slight cold. Two
days later, the doctor told the girls their father had a mild case
of pleurisy. There was no immediate danger, he assured, but
since Mr. Drexel was an important figure in the economy of his
country, his physicians took every precaution. Elizabeth received their orders as to treatment, diet, and medication, and
then divided other sickroom duties with Kate, who had appointed herself nurse.

Mr. Drexel submitted to the ministrations of the girls and,
ten days later, was allowed to leave his bed. Kate selected
several books from the family library and placed them on a
table near her father's favorite chair.

Though Miss Cassidy had continued her duties as a sort of
general manager, she often found herself cast in the old role
of teacher, as well. Her opinion on books, plays, and current
events was respected by all of the girls and, on Lincoln's
birthday, 1885, over a late lunch with Kate, she was discuss-
ing the merits of "Old Abe," both as President and as Great
Emancipator. Suddenly they heard the organ. At first the
music was so soft they both thought they were imagining it.
Then a swell of beautiful notes seemed to echo throughout
the house.

"He must be better," Miss Cassidy murmured in surprise. "I
haven't heard such a joyful note in his music since your
mother's death. There's strength there, too. He isn't simply
touching the keys."

"There's power in the pedal movements," Kate observed,
beginning to grow anxious. "The doctors want him to be quiet
and avoid any exertion. As happy as I am to hear the music

again—I know how much the organ means to him—we can't risk a setback. We'd better get him back to his room."

Kate jumped up, but Miss Cassidy remained seated. "You're anxious, of course," she said quietly, as she gently held Kate's arm and drew the young woman down into her chair again, "but you know that neither of us would dare to interrupt your father when he is at his organ. Wait until the music stops; then help him to his room."

"You're right," Kate admitted. "Now that Papa is out of danger, I should be less anxious, but I'm so afraid something might happen to him. If he died—I think I should die, too!"

"Kate Drexel!" Miss Cassidy rose and faced her former pupil sternly. "I'm surprised at you! Don't forget that your father has been very lonely these past two years. And when you're older, you'll understand that there are many things worse than dying. Loneliness is one of them."

"But Papa has always had us," Kate insisted though she was secretly ashamed that her emotions had betrayed her.

"Have you ever thought that there must have been times when he wondered whether Louise might have preferred being with that handsome young lawyer, Morrell, or that Elizabeth might have turned down invitations to accompany Walter George Smith and his sister to the theater?" Miss Cassidy pressed her advantage. "And he knows that one of the reasons—though I'm not saying it is the only one—you have not decided what you are going to do with your life is because you are clinging to him."

"How do you know all this?" Kate asked in surprise. "Did Papa ever tell you these things?"

"As time passes," Miss Cassidy said, smiling sadly, "you come to understand the thoughts of those you love—even when they are not put into words. And, Kate, I love you and your family very dearly."

"Oh, Miss Cass." Kate slipped into the greeting Louise sometimes used for their teacher. "You're a *part* of us! You're almost a Drexel. Nothing will ever separate us. And when Papa gets well, we're going to plan a trip and have you come with us. We'll go to Ireland with you; then we'll visit Assisi for me, and Elizabeth and Louise want to go to Spain. So we'll stop there, too, and we'll return to Rome. I'd like to have another audience with the Pope. Then we'll go to Annecy and see the house where Francis de Sales lived. He's Papa's patron saint, you know. We'll have one grand splurge and then..."

"And then what?"

"I'll pray," Kate began, "that I might..."

The door opened abruptly. "Where is Papa?" Elizabeth asked excitedly. "The moment we came into the house Louise and I both dropped our packages and ran up to his room, but he isn't there."

"Oh, we hadn't noticed that the music had stopped," Miss Cassidy said. "Your father has been at his organ. He's probably resting a bit before returning to his room."

"What a fright!" Elizabeth sank into a chair relieved. "Shopping with Louise is no easy task and I really overstayed my time. Then, when I didn't find him—I didn't know what to think."

"He's most likely in his room now," Miss Cassidy assured as Kate started up the stairs, "but I don't think you girls should let him see how anxious you are about him. Cheerfulness is important to a convalescent."

Kate was reluctant to leave her father alone after the incident on Lincoln's birthday. The following Sunday afternoon, she watched him as he selected one of the books she had placed on his table, adjusted his eyeglasses, and found the page he had marked.

After consulting the written directions Elizabeth had given her concerning a new medication for her father, Kate settled down to read until it was time for the patient's next dose. She had been reading for fifteen or twenty minutes when she looked up to find her father's eyes on her. He smiled, then removed his glasses and rose as if to walk toward her.

"Papa," Kate asked standing quickly, "is there something you'd like for me to get you?"

But, before his daughter could reach him, Francis Drexel slumped back into his chair. Beads of perspiration lined his brow, and Kate saw a sightless stare in his eyes.

"Elizabeth! Louise! Call the doctor!" Kate screamed as she ran down the stairs. "I'm going to Saint Patrick's for a priest!" Stopping in the hallway to grab a wrap, she rushed out the door.

Cutting through Rittenhouse Square, Kate ran as fast as she could. Bareheaded and with her open coat flapping in the wind, she was insensible to everything except her desire to get a priest for her father. She had seen death in his eyes; there was no need to hope. Panting, she ran up the steps of Saint Patrick's rectory, pushed past the maid who opened the door, and rushed into the parlor where a few priests were having a conference.

"Come quickly!" she cried breathlessly. "My father is dying!"

The priests were stunned and remained seated.

"My God!" Kate moaned, as she leaned against a wall, "my father is dying and they won't even come…"

Father Mulholland, who recognized Kate, now rose and went quickly to her side.

"Yes, yes, my child," he said calmly. "I shall come at once."

As through a veil, Kate saw the priest leave while other figures moved around her. She heard a familiar voice, and after a while recognized Mary Jane, one of the Drexel servants.

"Come with me, Miss Kate," the woman kept saying. "Come with me."

"Papa? How's my father?"

"I heard you talking to your sister," Mary Jane told her, "so I took a cab to Saint John's and got a priest. The driver waited and I came over here for you."

One of the priests helped Kate to the cab and within minutes they were home. Suddenly there was a flicker of hope, and Kate's legs, which seemed to have turned to rubber, were strong again. She ran up the steps to her father's room, then stopped at the threshold.

He was lying in bed, straight and still. His eyes were closed, and a man leaned over the inert form. Quickly she walked over to the bed. Then she knew that her father was dead.

Kate heard Louise and then Elizabeth speak to her. But the room seemed to be filled with people whose faces she couldn't distinguish. She lost track of time and movement, but she knew they were talking about her when a voice said, "She's gone into shock."

Francis Anthony Drexel died on February 15, 1885. He was buried the following Thursday from Saint Mary's Church, and his mortal remains were placed temporarily in the Bouvier vault at Saint Mary's churchyard.

The Drexel sisters received letters and telegrams of condolence from all over the United States and Europe. Mr. Drexel had made numerous friends through his own firm in Philadelphia; through Drexel, Morgan & Company in New York; and through Drexel, Harjes & Company in Paris. Though such notables as former-President Grant and outstanding members of literary, musical, and philanthropic circles mourned Mr. Drexel's passing, it was the poor whose grief most touched the hearts of those he had left behind.

People stood outside the church and endured a biting wind when the body was taken to the vault. Those who had never met Francis Drexel in their lives wept without shame. They didn't know that the friend they mourned had left the bulk of his vast fortune to God's needy. No one knew, or could know, of the heroic manner in which the good works begun by Francis Anthony Drexel and his wife, Emma, would go on and on.

Hannah Langstroth
Drexel, Katharine's
birth mother

Francis Anthony
Drexel

Emma Bouvier Drexel

Katharine and Elizabeth Drexel at ages five and seven

The three Drexel sisters: Katharine, age seven and a half, Louise, age two and a half, and Elizabeth, age ten and a half

Katharine
at seven

Katharine
at twenty

Two views of Katharine and Elizabeth's bedroom
at 1503 Walnut Street

Mr. and Mrs. Drexel's room

The family's oratory

Saint Michel's, the Drexel's summer home
at Torresdale, Pennsylvania

Bishop James O'Connor, Katharine's spiritual director

(Photo on the next page) Katharine met
Sioux Indian Chief Red Cloud (center)
during her 1887 visit to South Dakota's Pine
Bluff Reservation. Red Cloud was a great
leader and a courageous Catholic. Note the
crosses on his native dress.

Katharine at thirty

Mother Katharine, newly professed

Mother Katharine with Navajo silversmiths on
a reservation in Keams Canyon, Arizona, 1927

Saint Catherine's Boarding School, Santa Fe, New Mexico,
was the sisters' first missionary foundation

Mother
Katharine
with Mr. John
Moore of
Lake Charles,
Louisiana

Mother Katharine with Navajo Indian and Franciscan priest
at Lukachukai, Arizona, 1920

Mother Katharine with children of Xavier University graduates

Mother Katharine and friends

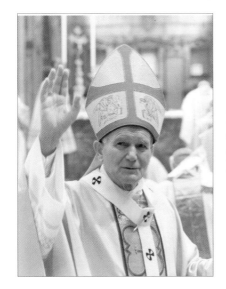

Pope John Paul II
during the beatification
ceremonies on
November 20, 1988

Overview of Saint Peter's Basilica during the beatification Mass

Scenes from the beatification:

Dr. Norman C. Francis,
President of Xavier University

Marie Tso Allen, Navajo

Mr. and Mrs. Morris
of Houston, Texas,
greet Pope John
Paul

Sisters of the Blessed
Sacrament present at
Saint Peter's

Pope John Paul II with Robert Gutherman. Robert's cure was the miracle accepted for Mother Katharine's beatification.

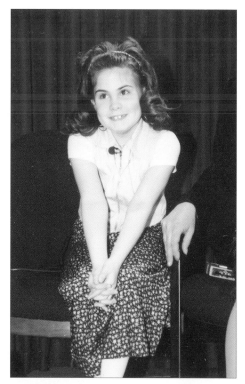

Amy Wall. Amy's healing was officially recognized as the miracle required for Mother Katharine's canonization.

Amy with her mother, Constance, and Cardinal Anthony Bevilacqua of Philadelphia

Chapter 9

The Key Is Found

There was a quiet determination on the part of the three Drexel sisters that life at 1503 Walnut Street should continue as their parents would have liked. The Dorcas and all other charities were carried on with painstaking diligence. The girls were especially concerned about orphans, for their father's loving care of unfortunate children was one of the dominating interests of his life. In his will, he had made liberal bequests to many orphanages, but the girls sought to continue his personal interest as well.

Elizabeth took the initiative in planning for future Drexel projects, while Louise contributed her boundless supply of energy. The shock of her father's death had left Kate's health so impaired that, in the early months of planning, she could contribute only her prayers.

Kate was almost sure that she should embrace the religious life. She even felt drawn to a contemplative nun's life of prayer and sacrifice. Bishop O'Connor, however, seemed convinced that she should continue helping others as she was doing—as a lay woman—not as a religious. Every time she asked his advice as to the direction her life should take, in the light of God's will, his counsel was always, "Think, wait, pray." Kate struggled to obey. The only bright spot in her life at this time was the

pleasure she derived from helping Father Hylebos and his Indian missions.

More and more, she yearned to talk with the man who was
then known as the "Prisoner of the Vatican." The kindness
and wisdom she had seen in the gentle smile of Leo XIII had
kindled a great hope in her heart. Kate tried hard to rise above
her personal problems, but she had lost interest in all else. The
more she labored to reach a decision about her vocation, the
more her health suffered.

Since the death of his brother, Anthony J. Drexel had
thrown a protective arm around his three nieces, and it was
after a conference with Uncle Anthony that Louise and Elizabeth approached Kate about the possibility of touring Europe
again.

"I want to establish a vocational school for orphan boys
as a memorial to Papa," Elizabeth confided to Kate. "Uncle
Anthony tells me there are many such institutions in Europe.
We could learn how to conduct such a school, and then we
could visit a German health resort where you could take advantage of the mineral baths."

"Oh Kate, it would do you a world of good," Louise coaxed.
"And Uncle Anthony knows just the spot. He says he's going
there for a rest as soon as he feels the bank can spare him."

"I'd like to go to Europe," Kate admitted, "but I'm not sure
I feel up to it yet, and I hadn't thought of going to Germany."

"You've always wanted to go to Assisi." Louise couldn't
conceal her eagerness. "We could stop there after the health
resort. We could even visit Rome again."

Perhaps, Kate thought, *this is the answer to my prayers.* She
knew that her family was concerned about her health, and she
hated to cause them added worry. "Where," she asked, "are the
German baths my kindest of uncles has recommended?"

"Schwalbach—between Eltzville and Wiesbaden," Louise quickly replied, "and Dr. DaCosta knows a doctor there who will look after you. In a month's time you'll be as good as new!"

It was impossible for Kate to resist, and in a few moments, all three of them were making plans for the trip.

Though the sisters were anxious to complete plans for the establishment of the vocational school, it was months before they found a site that met their uncle's approval. Kate and Louise were pleased that the 200-acre tract, which Elizabeth selected, was at Eddington, not far from Saint Michel's. After much deliberation they decided that the institution should be named Saint Francis de Sales Industrial School in honor of the learned saint who had been their father's patron. With the help of their uncle, a general outline for the school had been drawn up and the plans for the building were complete before the sisters set out for Europe.

Miss Cassidy considered it her duty to remain at home while they were away. She also recommended that Martin, the valet, should accompany the girls. "You've never traveled alone," she reminded them, "and I don't think your father would want you to do so now—especially with Kate's poor health." Their uncle seconded the recommendation and, as usual, Johanna was included in the traveling party. They sailed for Europe on July 31, 1886.

The sea voyage proved helpful for Kate and, upon their arrival in Schwalbach, the Drexels sought out the doctor who had been recommended. Within a day or two, the gentleman had familiarized himself with Kate's symptoms and she had begun the cure, which consisted of daily baths at the mineral springs and a glass of water from the Weinbrunner Spring twice a day.

Schwalbach was situated in the heart of the Nassau hill and forest country. Quaint villages with picturesque walks and drives dotted the countryside. Johanna always remained with Kate, whether she was at the baths or resting in the hotel. This provided Elizabeth and Louise with a great deal of time for walking and sightseeing. There was hardly a village in the region that the two didn't visit while Kate was, as she later said, "luxuriating in mud baths and quaffing off cups that cure." After five weeks, the doctor dismissed the patient, who reflected the effectiveness of his Schwalbach *kur*.

From Schwalbach Kate and her sisters, together with Johanna and Martin, traveled southward through the Rhine Valley. As they drove through the Black Forest, an evening haze, spangled by flickering darts of golden light, hung over the irregular ranges. Kate felt her soul expanding in praise of the One who had created such startling beauty.

Once more, the Drexels stopped at Bern. Then it was on to Interlaken. There Kate felt the need to rest for a few days and draw strength from the snow-capped Jangfrau. Each morning as she knelt at Mass, she offered prayers of thanksgiving. *I know,* she told herself over and over, *that God has given us this time of repose in order to form our plans.*

One day in a foggy rain the girls made the ascent to Murren, situated on a terrace over 5,000 feet high. As they climbed higher and higher, Kate felt a great joy. That night she set down in her journal some of the reflections that had flooded her being as she stood poised halfway between heaven and earth. "I felt as if I were standing at the Day of Judgment," she wrote. "Man's life span is like the passing of a cloud over the unchanging mountains."

After visiting an industrial school at Geneva, they went on to Annecy where Saint Francis de Sales, patron of the school the Drexels would establish, had once lived.

Johanna had not been enthusiastic over the mountain-climbing trips, which Kate and her sisters enjoyed, but she was always with them when they made pilgrimages. Kate was delighted that the older woman (for the Joe of fiery temper, quick tongue, and big heart was no longer young) enjoyed walking with them over the same streets that Saint Francis de Sales had walked 300 years before.

They visited the church where Francis had preached—a large Gothic structure—and rang the front doorbell of the house where he had lived for twelve years. They also visited the chapel of the Visitation Convent, founded by Saint Jane Frances de Chantal, the noblewoman for whom Saint Francis de Sales had been both spiritual director and friend. As Kate knelt before the altar near the relics of her father's patron, which rested in a large marble sarcophagus, she couldn't help wishing that her father could be there with them.

Gold lamps hung around the side of the circular sanctuary. The girls learned that it was the custom to make an offering and have a candle burning for a year before the saint's relics. Kate sought out the sacristan and gave him a fifty-franc note. "For the intentions and good health of all my relatives and friends," she told him.

As Kate and her sisters left the church, Joe rushed in from the vestibule. "You might have told me those candles burn a year," she scolded. "You know Madame Moran would feel slighted if I passed up a chance to get a whole year of prayers for her." The girls smiled at Joe's thoughtfulness for Madame

Moran, one of the religious of the Sacred Heart at Eden Hall, whose friendship Johanna had cherished since the days of her novitiate.

Kate wasn't sure what she expected to happen in Assisi. The sun shone brightly enough on the little town perched on the crest of a rocky hill where Francis Bernardone had grown up. The air was balmy, and she inhaled a certain fragrance as they rode past orange and olive groves. Almost as if in a dream, Kate heard her sisters commenting on the beauty of the fruit and flowers they passed by. But her attention was focused on her one desire to visit the chapel of Saint Mary of the Angels, the Portiuncula, where the son of the wealthy Peter Bernardone had learned through a revelation what his way of life was to be.

The guide showed Kate and her sisters various places associated with the saint of Assisi. They were taken to the beautiful basilica that had been built in his honor. Kate knelt before the relics and prayed, but even then she was distracted by the desire to reach the Portiuncula, Francis' "Little Portion." Elizabeth and Louise sensed Kate's impatience and, at the whispered urging of Joe, suggested that the party set out for the Portiuncula without delay.

Kate stood outside the Portiuncula for a moment and prayed that she, too, might be blessed with a revelation—that she might understand the special work God had in mind for her. Through the Dorcas she had seen the suffering of God's poor. During the months when the Drexels resided at their Walnut Street home, Elizabeth and two of her friends conducted a Sunday school for the African American children at old Saint Joseph's, and she talked often of their poverty. Every letter from Father Hylebos made Kate more aware of the need for schools and churches for the Native Americans. Two priests who were connected with the Bureau of Indian Affairs had visited the Drexels before they left for Europe to beg support for these countless neglected Americans.

Yet what can I do to help them, Kate thought, *when I'm not sure what I must do with my own life?* Then she remembered Saint Francis' many attempts to go as a crusader to the Mohammedans of the East and how he later sent missionaries to Tunisia. An inspiration suddenly came to her. *Perhaps I can ask the Holy Father to send missionaries to the Indians.* She smiled, unaware that the miracle of grace was already at work as she walked into the chapel where Francis had once knelt.

The revelation Kate had hoped for did not come in the way she had expected. While she knelt in the Portiuncula pondering the words of Saint Matthew's Gospel, "Freely have you received; freely give," which had been accepted by Francis as his Rule, she knew only that she, who had freely received, must also freely give. A great impatience possessed her, and it seemed as if the birds outside the windows of the chapel were singing, "Rome! Rome! Rome!"

Kate's sisters were worried. They were afraid that the Assisi visit had been unsuccessful, that they had waited too long and that Kate had built up too many expectations. For the first time since the cure at Schwalbach their sister was listless and showed little interest in the food set before them at mealtimes.

Kate was silent on the trip to Rome, but Elizabeth and Louise kept reminding her that their old friend, Miss Carrere, would be there to meet them.

Kate's lethargy was of short duration, though. When they reached Marseilles and their former French teacher, Mademoiselle de Saint Marsault, joined the party, Kate was as talkative and cheerful as either of her sisters.

It was like a homecoming when Kate and her sisters saw Miss Carrere—their beloved Caro—waiting for them at the station. Through various connections, the request for an audience with Pope Leo XIII had been made, and each day Kate hoped to receive word that permission for an audience with His Holiness had been granted.

It's almost like holding your breath, she thought one night when sleep was slow to come. *This is what I've waited for, and yet, there is so much work to be done in this world. I don't know where to start; I can't be all things to all people. Still, I don't know which people are to be my special charge.*

Kate and her sisters had found several stacks of mail waiting upon their arrival in Rome. Those from Father Hylebos brought tears to Kate's eyes. There had been a terrible drought and many of the Native Americans were now starving. In another letter, Bishop O'Connor was already asking Kate if she felt free to share the result of her audience with the Holy Father. And each morning she faced a new day hopefully expecting to learn that tomorrow might be the one she had long awaited.

The summons finally came. On January 27, 1887, Kate and her party were granted the privilege of participating at Mass celebrated by the Pontiff. Afterward, they were to have a private audience with him. When Elizabeth and Louise reminded Joe to watch her behavior, Kate almost weakened in her determination to speak with the Holy Father.

Johanna checked the sisters' black dresses and veils to make sure they were clothed according to the requirements of the time. When the carriage arrived, Kate was so excited she felt as if her knees would buckle. After they were shown into the chapel, she could hardly remember how they had gotten there. She kept wondering if anything would happen to keep the aging pontiff from celebrating that particular Mass or from granting them the promised audience. Her head was bowed when the revered celebrant approached the altar, but when she looked up and saw him, all doubts and fears vanished. A calm settled over Kate, which lasted throughout the Mass.

When they were ushered into the reception room, she was the one who appeared least nervous. Each of them knelt in turn to kiss the papal ring and to receive the blessing of their spiritual father. Then Elizabeth, as the eldest, asked the Pope if he would send a blessing to their relatives and friends in America. At that point, Kate felt the Holy Father's eyes upon her. The friendliness in his gaze gave her the courage she had prayed for.

I must tell His Holiness about the Indians and about the hardships Father Hylebos encounters in the Northwest, she thought.

Johanna couldn't resist the temptation to speak of the many good works of Francis and Emma Drexel and of how, since their death, the Drexel sisters were trying to carry on their parents' charities. To the astonishment of her sisters, Kate then stepped forward and proceeded to give a detailed account of the sufferings of the American Indians and of the hardships endured by priests who worked with them. The Pope leaned toward her as if to hear better and Kate felt she had captured his interest.

"Your Holiness," she finished, "the Indians are starving for spiritual, as well as material, food. Oh, Holy Father, I beg you to send missionaries to them."

The Pope searched the face of the impassioned young woman who stood before him. Neither the wealth nor the charity of the Drexels was unknown to him. He closed his eyes for a moment. When Leo XIII opened them again, the beauty of his smile seemed to wipe out all trace of the many years that had bestowed such great wisdom upon him. "Why," he asked, "don't you become a missionary yourself, my child?"

Here in the Eternal City, at the feet of the supreme Pontiff, Katharine Mary Drexel received the challenge that would lead her to her true vocation. But, at that instant, the Pope's unexpected answer was such a shock that she suddenly felt terribly frightened and sick—so sick, she confided to one of the Sisters of the Blessed Sacrament many years later, that she rushed out of the Vatican in tears.

The scene would almost repeat itself in November of that same year when Thérèse Martin, a young woman half Kate's age, would kneel before Pope Leo to beg his special permission to enter Carmel at the age of fifteen. She who would someday be known to the world as Saint Thérèse of Lisieux would also leave the audience in tears.

What had Pope Leo *really* meant? Kate didn't know, and the confusion, coupled with her grief at the loss of her parents, threatened to overwhelm her. She thought. She waited. She prayed.

Chapter 10

A Time for Parting

Though the Drexels stopped at Paris and London before sailing for America, Kate was already looking forward to another trip, one which would take her to the Northwest—home to numerous Native Americans, and where she hoped to further clarify her vocation.

Kate warned her sisters and Johanna not to mention her conversation with Pope Leo XIII to anyone. She feared the news might be spread, or be reported inaccurately, before she could truly discern God's will.

Soon after they returned to Saint Michel's, Kate announced her intention to visit the Indians, and her sisters promptly offered to make the trip with her.

While the Drexels had been in Europe, the cornerstone for Saint Francis de Sales Industrial School at Eddington, Pennsylvania had been laid. Now Elizabeth set about making plans for the dedication ceremony, which was to take place within the next year.

Louise was busy with her own project. She had become interested in the new Saint Joseph's Society, an order of priests devoted to the care of African Americans. While Kate was seeking advice from priests working with the Native Americans, Louise was familiarizing herself with the work of the Josephites.

Thus, all of the Drexel sisters had now found channels through which they could share the worldly goods bequeathed them by their generous parents.

Kate envisioned helping the Native Americans on a much broader scale than Father Hylebos' missions. On the advice of Bishop O'Connor, she sought out Bishop Martin Marty, O.S.B., then vicar apostolic of Northern Minnesota—later bishop of Sioux Falls, South Dakota—and Father Joseph A. Stephan, director of the Bureau of Catholic Indian Missions in Washington. The Drexel sisters had already donated generously to these two priests. From these two men Kate learned more about the specific needs of the Indians. She ended by pledging them her wholehearted support.

From time to time collections for the Native Americans were taken up in the churches of Philadelphia, and among Kate's family members and friends it became a standing joke that she would not allow one of them to escape. A fond relative once said that Kate's pocketbook was so heavy on the Sundays these collections were taken up that she had difficulty carrying it from the carriage to the church! He admitted, too, that he had allowed "the sweet benefactress" to empty his own pockets for her worthy cause.

Pleased that the Drexel sisters wanted to visit the Indian missions, in spite of the hardships the trip would entail, Father Stephan hastened to invite them to visit Native American settlements in his territory.

They set out in mid-September, 1887, and would be gone for almost a full month. Their first stop was Omaha, Nebraska, where they met with Bishop O'Connor. The bishop was delighted with Kate's enthusiasm for the Indian missions. But he was still unconvinced of her religious vocation. He continued praying in order to discern God's will in her regard.

As Kate talked of the great need of the "neglected and despised Indians" and of the shameful way they had been treated, the bishop reminded her that the Indians were not the only neglected and despised group: African Americans shared the same fate.

Listening to the bishop speak, Kate recalled what Louise had once laughingly remarked: "You have only some hundred thousand souls in your Indian field, but I have ten or more million in my Negro harvest."

She also remembered a letter from Father Stephan in which he had described a Confirmation ceremony at an African American parish in Washington. Father Stephan had been asked to celebrate the High Mass because, as he said, the "Blacks and Indians are color relations."

That's right, Kate thought now. *They're all children of God, many of whom do not yet know his glory.* She began to nurture the idea of assisting African American as well as Native American missions.

After shopping for bright beads and trinkets to give to the Indians as gifts, the Drexels began their tour with Bishop O'Connor and Father Stephan. They traveled part of the way by train and then set out on the open trail. Elizabeth and Louise had brought their saddles and rode their horses while Kate traveled in the carriage with Bishop O'Connor and Father Stephan.

Four miles from Saint Francis Mission in Rosebud Agency, South Dakota, Kate and her sisters were thrilled by the colorful sight of six Native American police riding out to meet them. At the mission, Father Stephan presented Bishop O'Connor and the Drexel sisters to Chief Roast-Big-Turkey. "How"— probably a corruption of "How are you?"—seemed the favorite greeting. There was vigorous handshaking and much "howing."

These members of the Sioux tribe were the first Native Americans the Drexels had ever spoken with.

Inspired though she was Kate never lost her delightful sense of humor. Years later she laughingly recalled their first night at an Indian mission. Father Stephan had neglected to inform the Sisters of Saint Francis that he was bringing the bishop and a party of young ladies, so no preparations had been made for them. The mission had not been completed, but the nuns managed to improvise beds for the visitors on the first floor.

Uneasy and unable to sleep, the girls were grateful for the first signs of dawn. But, when they started to get out of bed, they found that there were neither shades, nor curtains at the windows. And pressed against the panes were several Indians' faces, their bright eyes peering at the strangers. The nuns laughingly chased the Indians away and "rescued" their guests.

They attended Mass at the mission church, which was also incomplete. The benches were mere boards without backs, and the Indians treated these makeshift seats as playthings, stepping from one to the other like joyful children. Their glee was contagious, and Kate laughed out before she realized it.

"But I sobered quickly," she recalled later, "when the holy Jesuit reprimanded the Indians for want of reverence to the Blessed Sacrament."

After Mass there was a general "howing," followed by an ox feast. Kate and her sisters gave out gifts to the Indian women who wore their brightly colored dresses and shawls, some of them with painted faces, most of them with infants strapped to their backs. Several of the men were wrapped in unbleached sheets, others in fancy costumes, and still others in European clothes that had been given to them. Kate never forgot the sight of the Native Americans flocking to the mission on foot, in wagons, and on horseback.

After Bishop O'Connor had returned to Omaha, Father Stephan led them on to Holy Rosary Mission, Pine Bluff Agency, and then to the Immaculate Conception Mission which Kate was having built as a loving tribute to her mother.

Sometimes by horseback, sometimes by rail, and more than once by wagon, Kate and her sisters visited mission after mission. Everywhere they traveled people pleaded for more sisters, more brothers, more priests.

It was late October when the Drexels finally returned to Saint Michel's, but not to rest, for it was after this trip that the many Drexel Indian Schools, as they were called, came into existence.

Not long before General Custer's last stand at the Little Big Horn, President Grant had announced he would give a subsidy of one-hundred dollars a pupil to any religious group which would establish schools among the Native Americans. The interest of Kate and her sisters was now stimulated by their trip and by their firsthand observation of the need for schools, churches, and religious to staff them.

With the advice of Father Stephan, Kate bought property, erected buildings, and then deeded the structures and grounds to the Bureau of Catholic Indian Missions. Father Stephan then received a contract from the government entitling the bureau to the promised subsidy for each student. The only remaining task facing Kate and Father Stephan was to storm heaven and the superiors of religious communities to supply priests and nuns.

As time went on, Kate became more and more certain of her call to religious life, despite Bishop O'Connor's continual words of caution that convent life might be too drastic a change from what she was used to. Finally, after receiving her impassioned letter of November 26, 1888, in which Kate revealed the anxiety and sadness she had been experiencing for two years as she tried to follow his advice, Bishop O'Connor had a complete change of heart. Four days later he wrote her a letter in which he withdrew all opposition to her entering the convent. He even suggested three religious orders she might consider joining. Kate responded that she didn't feel attracted to these communities and that she wanted "a missionary order for Indians and Colored people." It would take time to come to know God's will more clearly.

While Bishop O'Connor celebrated Mass on February of 1889, a forceful thought came to him: Kate herself should found a new religious congregation in the Church—one entirely dedicated to the service of Native and African Americans. He immediately shared this inspiration with her. Kate had her misgivings. She was still toying with the idea of becoming a contemplative and leaving her entire inheritance to the Black and Indian missions. She was also doubtful that she possessed the necessary qualities to found a new community. And so Kate continued to pray while the bishop continued to stress that this *was* God's will.

In the summer of 1888, the Most Reverend Patrick. J. Ryan, D.D., archbishop of Philadelphia, dedicated the Saint Francis de Sales Industrial School at Eddington. The pupils of the new complex, which was to be run by the Brothers of the Christian Schools, numbered some 200 boys selected from Saint John's Orphan Asylum in Philadelphia.

Meanwhile, Louise, whose interest in the Josephites had continued, bought for the order a $59,000 property in Baltimore. This was the beginning of Epiphany College, which was to train priests for work in the African American apostolate.

When the Drexel sisters were asked to support the projected Catholic University of America, they donated $50,000 for the establishment of the Francis A. Drexel chair of Moral

Theology. Another $30,000 went to Saint Agnes Hospital in Philadelphia in order that the Sisters of Saint Francis might buy property for the expansion of the hospital.

Although Kate and her sisters had little time to enjoy a social life, youth is a time for romance. The year their charitable works reached its peak was the very year Louise Bouvier Drexel quietly announced her engagement to Edward Morrell. Soon after the bells rang to usher in the New Year of 1889, wedding bells also echoed.

The Nuptial Mass at the cathedral was celebrated by Bishop O'Connor, with Archbishop Ryan presiding. Their dear uncle, Anthony Drexel, gave the bride away. Kate, Elizabeth, and their cousins Katherine Drexel and Lillie Dixon, were bridesmaids. Only relatives and a few intimate friends were invited to the breakfast at Walnut Street.

The year 1889 was also significant for Kate. On March 19, the feast of Saint Joseph, she finally felt at peace about her future. She finally knew—in her own heart—that what Bishop O'Connor had been telling her was true: her foundation of a new religious congregation *was* the will of God.

Elizabeth and Louise were happy that Kate had found her mission in life. With the day of their separation still indefinite, they brushed aside any thoughts of personal loss and accepted God's will. Joe, too, was happy. In a way, Kate's vocation would offset the disappointment she had always felt for having to leave the convent so many years before. And Miss Cassidy, who had long suspected Kate's vocation lay in the religious life, was relieved that the time of indecision was past.

Bishop O'Connor arranged for Kate to enter the novitiate of the Sisters of Mercy in Pittsburgh. There she would receive training in the religious life before beginning her own congregation to serve the Native and African Americans. After Louise's marriage, Kate dreaded leaving Elizabeth alone, but she was eager to get started. Although the schools she had built and supported for the Native Americans were going well, she was always aware of the need for more teachers. This was to be her special mission.

It was spring before the honeymooners—Louise and Ned Morrel—started homeward. The couple returned to Philadelphia, pausing only long enough to make plans for setting up their own homes at South Rittenhouse Square and on a property adjoining Saint Michel's which Louise had christened San José. Elizabeth, Louise, and Ned were to make the trip to the Pittsburgh convent with Kate, and from there, the three of them were to go on to Europe.

In the meantime, the three sisters were together again—with the addition of a new brother-in-law. Only the realization that Kate was leaving them to seek her own sanctification and to bring greater honor and glory to God softened the sorrow of what was to be a final parting of the ways.

On May 7, 1889, the family left Philadelphia. At Pittsburgh, Elizabeth, Louise, and Ned entrusted Kate to Mother Sebastian, the superior, and Mother Inez, the mistress of novices of the Sisters of Mercy. Kate radiated the joy of one who has at long last fulfilled the desire of her heart, and her sisters and new brother-in-law were consoled by that happiness. They were relieved, though, not to have to return to 1503 Walnut Street without her and grateful for their foresight in planning a trip to Europe.

With the permission of Mother Inez, the young postulant, now Sister Mary Katharine, wrote often to the travelers. She knew they were worried about her health, so she reassured them by writing cheerfully, and giving vivid pictures of her daily life. When she wasn't sure of their address, she sent her letters to faithful Johanna, who redirected them.

Sister Katharine's reception into the Sisters of Mercy was scheduled for November 7, 1889. Her family returned to the States in September, and Louise and Ned were delighted to find San José nearing its completion.

Elizabeth made all of the preparations for the trip to the Pittsburgh convent. With the aid of their Uncle Anthony, a private car was chartered on the Pennsylvania Railroad. Besides Elizabeth, Louise, and Ned, many of the Drexel and Bouvier aunts, uncles, and cousins, as well as a few intimate friends made up the traveling party.

Elizabeth and Louise, happy that Kate's reception was to be a festive occasion, were also saddened by comments from some of their relatives who made it clear that they thought Kate had been heartless to leave Elizabeth alone. Of course, they were unaware that the older sister had a secret of her own, one she had decided not to reveal until after Kate's reception.

Father Stephan was among those present on that memorable November day when Kate Drexel, radiant in her orange-blossom trimmed bridal gown and glittering jewels, left the chapel carrying her habit and returned wearing the black robe and white veil of a novice of the Sisters of Mercy. Archbishop Ryan presided at the ceremony and, for the first time, publicly revealed that Katharine would be the foundress of a new congregation in the Church. From that day on, her name in religion would be Sister Mary Katharine.

Newspaper reporters had sought interviews with the Drexel heiress from the day she had entered the convent, but Mother Inez and Mother Sebastian had shielded her from all publicity. They were even more careful at the time of the reception, and most of the wire services simply carried routine accounts of the ceremony, although some newspapers referred to Sister Katharine as "the world's richest nun."

On the return train ride to Philadelphia, Elizabeth Drexel revealed her secret to the rest of the family. She was engaged to Walter George Smith, a brilliant young attorney. They were quietly wed on January 7, 1890, in the little country church of Saint Dominic near Saint Michel's. Though Sister Katharine couldn't be present, she was grateful to God that her beloved sister wouldn't be alone or lonely. The last pebble had been removed from Kate's pool of spiritual joy. Nothing could, or would, distract her from the work to which God, his Blessed Mother, Saint Francis, the Holy Father, and Bishop O'Connor had directed her.

Chapter 11

On Fire with Love

The weeks passed swiftly for Sister Katharine. It wouldn't be long before Lady Poverty, for whom Saint Francis had held such great love, would become her daily companion. Surely, the young novice thought, her joy was boundless.

Meanwhile, Elizabeth and Louise were literally surveying the whole of Bucks County, Pennsylvania, in search of an appropriate site for the home of the new community Sister Katharine was to found. Shortly before Elizabeth left for her European honeymoon, she found a parcel of land at Andalusia—later to be called Cornwells Heights, and today Bensalem. Louise agreed it would be an ideal location for a Motherhouse. With Sister Katharine's approval, the property was purchased. Plans moved forward, and the ground was broken despite numerous threats from the surrounding neighbors, while Elizabeth was still on her honeymoon.

The building program was a happy excuse for the sisters to write each other often. There came a time, however, when no letters from the bride were delivered to the convent in Pittsburgh. Sister Katharine tried not to worry, yet it was so unlike the thoughtful Elizabeth. Then came a message from Louise: Elizabeth was dangerously ill—and there was an ocean and convent wall between them.

While Sister Katharine was storming heaven for her sister, Louise left for Europe. There were many days of anguished prayer until Sister Katharine heard that Elizabeth was out of danger.

The cup of sorrow was still not empty. In May 1890, Sister Katharine's spiritual director, Bishop O'Connor, answered the call of his Master. The seriously ill bishop had been welcomed into Mercy Hospital in Pittsburgh and the Sisters of Mercy had graciously allowed Sister Katharine to assist him as a kind of nurse's aide.

Bishop O'Connor's death threw the young novice into a painful spiritual crisis. He had suggested that she begin a new congregation to assist the Native and African Americans. Sister Katharine had only agreed to the idea knowing that he would be there to help her. Now she was alone. She felt totally helpless and discouraged. She wondered if she should give up the whole project.

But the Lord came to her rescue in the person of Archbishop Patrick Ryan of Philadelphia, a close friend of Bishop O'Connor's. Realizing what a blow the bishop's death must have been to Sister Katharine, he lost no time in getting in touch with her. After Bishop O'Connor's funeral Mass, Archbishop Ryan visited Sister Katharine at the convent. The grieving novice confided to him that she felt she could no longer go on with the foundation. The archbishop listened kindly. He leaned forward in his chair and asked, "If I share the burden with you, if I help you, can you go on?"

At these words, Sister Katharine felt new courage and hope flooding her soul. From that moment, Archbishop Ryan took Bishop O'Connor's place as her spiritual father, her confidant, and her support. Not long after, Sister Katharine also received the apostolic blessing of Pope Leo XIII. It was another confirmation of her vocation.

Not long after Bishop O'Connor's passing, the superior had the sad duty of delivering tragic news to Sister Katharine. Her sister, Elizabeth, just recently returned to Saint Michel's to await the birth of her first child, had suddenly joined Francis and Emma Drexel in death.

Louise was still on her way home from Europe, and when Sister Katharine reached Saint Michel's, she had to push aside her own grief to comfort the heartbroken husband who had lost both wife and child. She also had to console Miss Cassidy and Johanna who had been with Elizabeth until the end.

Returning to Pittsburgh for the last months of her novitiate, a small part of Sister Katharine's sorrow stemmed from the knowledge that Elizabeth's death had left Saint Michel's empty. So, it was just as well that many demands were made upon her time during the weeks that followed. Almost before she realized it, the day for which she had so longed for arrived—the day on which she would pronounce her vows and become a bride of Christ.

On February 12, 1891, in Saint Mary's Chapel of the Sisters of Mercy at Pittsburgh, Sister Mary Katharine made the vows of poverty, obedience, and chastity. She consecrated her life, and the fortune bequeathed her by her father, to the service of Native American and African Americans. Archbishop Ryan officiated at the ceremony. The archbishop immediately recognized Sister Katharine as the foundress of the new community that was to be known as the Sisters of the Blessed Sacrament for Indians and Colored People. As the first superior general of the congregation, she became Reverend Mother Mary Katharine Drexel.

Thirteen young women had answered Mother Katharine's call to prepare for this new work with the Native Americans and African Americans. More and more, the young superior's presence was required to supervise the construction work at the Motherhouse. Since Cornwells Heights was so near Saint Michel's, Mother Katharine decided to take her little band to Torresdale and use the Drexel home as a temporary novitiate until the new convent was completed. It was to be named Saint Elizabeth's in honor of her sister who had first shared plans for the building.

The laying of the cornerstone for the new Motherhouse took place on the afternoon of July 16, 1891. That morning the little community put on the new habit of the Sisters of the Blessed Sacrament for the first time. Mother Katharine had donned this habit at her first profession of vows, but she alone had been wearing it while the rest of the group continued to dress as postulants and novices of the Sisters of Mercy.

The happy young sisters were met with opposition and even hostility on the part of some. The sisters would only learn many years later of an angry attempt to stop the construction of their Motherhouse. The day before the dedication ceremony, workers had found a stick of dynamite near the spot where the cornerstone was to be laid. This was evidently the work of some of the neighboring farmers who were prejudiced against the sisters and the prospect of their service to the Indians and African Americans. The discovery was reported to Archbishop Ryan and, not wanting to frighten the sisters, he ordered that they were not to be told.

Mr. James Burns, the architect, devised a plan of his own to scare off the perpetrators. He filled a long wooden box with broomsticks and nailed the lid shut. On the outside of the box, in large letters, he printed this warning: DO NOT TOUCH, HIGHLY EXPLOSIVE NITROGLYCERINE. He then assigned one of the workmen to guard the box carefully all that day, instructing him to keep everyone from coming near it since the least vibration could trigger an explosion. The plan worked. When word of the dangerous box spread, the neighboring farmers kept their distance. Even the workman was convinced he was guarding dangerous explosives!

Fortunately, this incident ended well, but it was only one of the many instances of bigotry and opposition that Mother Katharine and the Sisters of the Blessed Sacrament would face in the coming years.

By the fall of 1892, the Motherhouse was ready, and there, in the archdiocese of Philadelphia, one of the greatest missionary efforts in the history of America began. As Mother Katharine's band grew, she continued to travel from one end of America to the other, setting up missions and schools.

Mother Katharine was especially concerned about the spiritual and material poverty of the Navajo Indians. Thousands of Navajo Indians roamed the Arizona desert on a twelve-million-acre reservation that was, for the greater part, simply barren waste. The foundress of the Blessed Sacrament Sisters was determined to build a school.

By the fall of 1902, the buildings that were to become Saint Michael's Boarding School were nearing completion, and Mother Katharine started for Arizona to prepare living quarters for those who were to follow. After a stop at Santa Fe, where she and another sister visited a school already founded for the Pueblo Indians, they went on to Gallup, New Mexico. This was as far as the train would take them. After being met by a Franciscan priest, whose rectory was near the new school, they went on to Arizona. The Franciscans had been sent to work among the Navajos as a result of Mother Katharine's pleas for priests.

For the thirty-mile drive out to Saint Michael's, the priest had brought a light, horse-drawn spring wagon with two plank seats and no cover. If Mother Katharine compared the rattling wagon with the luxurious private car in which the Drexels had made their first trip deep into the West, she gave no sign of it. Any discomfort was soon forgotten as Mother Katharine and Mother Ignatius admired the stark beauty of the hills and valleys as they rode into the heart of the desert wilderness.

It seemed to Mother Katharine that the horses were treading an ocean of sand. The red sandstone cliffs dwarfed the animals as well as the wagon and its occupants. As the sun sank behind the cliffs, Mother Katharine fingered the beads hanging from her white cincture.

It's so easy, she thought, *to pray the rosary when one seems so alone with God.*

Though the sun had disappeared when the party reached the priests' home, a bright moon silvered the sandy hill on which the house stood. The sisters needed no lantern to find the path to the buildings, which were to become Saint Michael's.

Rooms for the sisters had been prepared in one of the cabins that had housed the workers. Enough moonlight shone into the dark log hut to allow Mother Katharine to find a lamp—but it was empty. After discovering oil and matches, the sisters lit the lamp and looked around. The lamp rested on a square kitchen table in the middle of the room, and the only other furnishing was an armchair. The floor would never need to be scrubbed or waxed—it was dirt-hard, even, and compact. The tiny adjoining room was bare except for two cots.

The next day Mother Katharine learned that the region had suffered a drought and that the corn she had instructed a farmer to plant had not come up. She had depended on the shucks from this corn to serve as stuffing for the hundred or more mattresses they would need for the Indian children.

Mother Katharine was also told that the men had been unable to find water except for the shallow well, which barely supplied the priests. She immediately wrote the Motherhouse and asked the sisters to pray for water and mattress stuffing. Then she dispatched one of the workmen to Gallup with instructions to go on to Santa Fe if necessary, to find the proper machinery to drill for water.

As a substitute for the shucks from the corn that never grew, Mother Katharine decided to try sheared wool. After a half-pound was secured for the test, it had to be washed. Back and forth from the priests' well the sisters carried bucket after bucket of water. Four times they rubbed and washed the wool with a mole plant, but the sheepy smell defied water and soap. They had been so engrossed in their experiment that neither sister noticed they had been spilling water. By the time they did notice, the floor was a huge muddy puddle. After a half-day's work, all the sisters had to show was the unpleasant-smelling wool and two pairs of mud-spattered black shoes.

The water situation remained serious. When it seemed almost hopeless, Mother Katharine asked one of the priests to drive her to the nearest church at Newton. As she begged God for water, she thought about our Lord sitting wearily at the well in Samaria and asking the woman to give him to drink. She remembered that he had said, "If you knew the gift of God and who it is that is saying to you, 'Give me a drink,' you would have asked him and he would have given you living water."

"O Lord," Mother Katharine prayed, "forgive me for asking

for temporal water rather than waters of abundant grace for the missionaries and the waters of baptism for the Navajos."

A few evenings later, Mother Katharine sat in the little dirt-floored cabin studying plans for the badly needed water system. Suddenly she heard the sound of trickling water. A stream was advancing across the floor toward her. The drought was over; rain had come. On the feast of Saint Michael, September 29, 1902, Mother Katharine directed the men who drilled successfully for water.

The hundreds of Navajo boys and girls, who have attended Saint Michael's, now a modern elementary and high school, enjoy an abundance of temporal, as well as spiritual, waters. This is the legacy they received from Mother Katharine and the Sisters of the Blessed Sacrament.

Great distances had to be spanned to reach the Native Americans, but needy African Americans were ever at Mother Katharine's door. Even during the days of the temporary novitiate at Saint Michel's, a group of African American orphans had been housed in the gardener's cottage. These children were the first to occupy Holy Providence House, which became a boarding school for African American children.

At the turn of the century, Mother Katharine realized the need to prepare African American girls to go out and work among their own people. She purchased a tract of land at Rock Castle, forty miles from Richmond, Virginia, near the home of the Indian maiden, Pocahontas. This site, on the southern bank of the historic James River, became the home of Saint Francis de Sales Institute, later Saint Francis de Sales High School. The massive red brick building was soon known as "The Castle." Here thousands of African American girls were educated.

Mrs. Morrell and her husband, continuing to share every interest of their saintly sister, purchased a vast estate, Belmead, about a mile away from Saint Francis de Sales. This sprawling old plantation became the home of Saint Emma Industrial and Agricultural Institute where African American boys were instructed in crafts and trades.

In June of 1904, Bishop Thomas Byrne of Nashville, Tennessee asked Mother Katharine to open a school for African American children in his diocese. During a personal meeting with her, he outlined his plans in detail, even down to the property he had in mind—property owned by a wealthy Nashville banker known neither for his concern for nor fondness toward African Americans. If Mother Katharine were to buy this property, he advised it would be best to do so through a third party.

After getting the bishop to agree that the school would be open to all African American children, not only to Catholics as he had originally proposed, Mother Katharine purchased the estate through Thomas J. Tyne, a Nashville attorney, on February 2, 1905.

Everything was fine until a local paper, *The Banner of Nashville*, revealed the identity of the *real* purchaser in an article published on February 13. Then a storm of protest broke loose. The former owner was enraged that his home was to become a school for African American girls. He wrote letters to the newspaper, to the attorney, to the bishop, and to Mother Katharine herself, offering to buy back the property. He even offered to contribute the commission he had made on the original sale. When these attempts failed, he promised to donate $2,500 to any Catholic organization that would buy the estate from Mother Katharine. No one accepted the offer and so, in desperation, the owner tracked down a dated, erroneous city plan that showed a street running through the middle of his old home. The street, of course, had never existed, but the irate man successfully gathered fifty signatures petitioning the mayor and city council to run one through the property!

As the criticism and opposition continued, Mother Katharine calmly went ahead with her plans. It wasn't the first time, and it wouldn't be the last, that she would encounter prejudice. As always, she conquered it with love. On September 5, 1905, the Immaculate Mother Academy and Industrial School opened its school year with a Mass celebrated by Bishop Byrne. By the end of that first year, there were over one hundred students enrolled.

In 1915, the archbishop of New Orleans, Most Reverend James S. Blenk, asked Mother Katharine to undertake the education of Black youth in New Orleans. Southern University had moved to Baton Rouge, and Mother Katharine purchased the vacated property for the new Xavier Secondary School, the forerunner of Xavier University. This proved to be a reliving of the Nashville drama. Again, racial prejudice made it necessary for a third party to purchase the property; again, the neighbors protested; again racial hatred reared its ugly head. And once again, Mother Katharine's love was victorious.

Xavier University, a coeducational institution for African Americans, soon became a reality. Now located at Drexel Drive and Carrollton Avenue, Xavier occupies approximately eight city blocks. The university comprises a college of liberal arts and sciences, a college of pharmacy, a school of education, a graduate school, and seven special departments. It remains a flourishing, integrated school open to young people of every race and creed.

Beginning in 1923, Mother Katharine went on to build twenty-four rural Catholic schools for African American children throughout Louisiana. She arranged for two Xavier graduates to be put in charge of each school and she also paid the salaries of all the teachers. Mother Katharine even arranged to pay additional salaries for teachers working in schools where the state provided education for African Americans only four or five months out of the year. As she had done for the Native Americans, she strove to help Blacks overcome economic disadvantages through education. She would continue to battle racial discrimination with her prayers, her work, and with the very witness of her life.

As African Americans crowded urban centers during the northern migrations following World War I, Mother Katharine sent her teaching daughters into these cities to staff parochial schools.

The steady progress of the missionary work of the Sisters of the Blessed Sacrament among the African Americans moved side by side with their efforts among the Native Americans. A spokesman for the Bureau of Catholic Indian Missions once said that every Catholic mission for Native Americans had, at one time or another, been aided by Mother Katharine Drexel.

While personally living a very simple and austere life in accordance with her vow of poverty, Mother Katharine held her millions in trust for the Indians and African Americans. This was the arrangement that had been made upon her entrance into religious life. Bishop O'Connor believed that she, more than anyone else, would be able to distribute the funds to those in greatest need. In 1921, Congress passed a law—and some say it was with Mother Katharine's fortune in mind—which freed charitable contributions from taxation!

Whenever a polite reference was made to the vast wealth Mother Katharine had renounced, she was quick to remind her listeners that she had given up only what every other Sister of the Blessed Sacrament had given up—everything she had. As missions were opened in Nashville, New Orleans, New York,

Philadelphia, Boston, Cleveland, Cincinnati, and Port Arthur, Mother Katharine continued to shun publicity and public attention. "It's better to do things quietly," she never tired of repeating.

Mother Katharine denied herself many of the same material comforts she so carefully provided for each of her daughters. It is said that the foundress of the Sisters of the Blessed Sacrament was always that nun who looked least the way people expected her to. Mother Katharine wore the habit given her until it was threadbare. On visitations to the far-flung Indian missions, she preferred a day coach to the comforts of a Pullman. She usually carried her lunch neatly wrapped in brown paper.

The Rule of the new congregation received the Decree of Final Approbation on May 15, 1913, during the pontificate of Pope Saint Pius X. Mother Katharine also received letters of commendation for her work and that of her congregation from Popes Benedict XV, Pius XI, and Pius XII.

Chapter 12

Hidden Contemplative

The labors and sacrifices of the years gradually took their toll on Mother Katharine's health. In August of 1935, she experienced a slight heart attack while praying at the bedside of one of her dying sisters. Another attack followed in 1936.

In 1937, she retired as superior general of her congregation. But even as her body aged, her spirit remained young. This was Mother Katharine's time for more intense prayer. It seemed that the Lord in his graciousness was now granting her the contemplative vocation she had dreamed of in her youth. She was able to spend longer hours in prayer and adoration, especially before Jesus in the Blessed Sacrament.

A happy occasion occurred during Mother Katharine's long retirement: the fiftieth anniversary of the foundation of her congregation in 1941. On February 12, fifty years before, Katharine Drexel had pronounced her vows as a Sister of the Blessed Sacrament.

At first, Mother Katharine, who had a real aversion to drawing attention to herself, opposed plans for any public celebration. It took Cardinal Dennis Dougherty to change her mind! Since the cardinal would be away in February, the jubilee celebration was set for April. Lasting three days, it drew hundreds of African Americans and Native Americans who might never have come to know and love God without the help of Mother Katharine and her daughters.

Mother Katharine spent the last twenty years of her life as a hidden contemplative. Her world was limited to two rooms on the second floor of the Motherhouse. But from there, her prayerful heart constantly visited her many missions scattered throughout the country.

One of her rooms had a small window that opened onto the chapel. It was also equipped with a ramp, which allowed her to be taken in a wheelchair to a mezzanine floor rising from the sanctuary of the chapel and set off by a decorative iron grille. As long as she was physically able, the foundress spent long hours praying here. Her nights, too, were filled with prayer. Her personal notes reveal that she had obtained permission from her superiors to make nocturnal hours of adoration from her bed, uniting herself spiritually to Jesus in the Blessed Sacrament.

In 1943, Cardinal Dougherty gave special permission for daily Mass to be celebrated in Mother Katharine's room. The altar was sent by the Religious of the Sacred Heart. It was the same simple altar at which Mother Katharine had received her First Communion long years before.

The death of her sister, Louise Drexel Morrell, in November of 1945 brought Mother Katharine new sorrow. Louise was the last surviving member of her immediate family. Mother Katharine struggled to accept the loss, but admitted that she didn't want "anything different from what God wants."

With Louise's death, Mother Katharine became the sole recipient of the income from an accumulated twenty-million dollar trust fund left to the Drexel daughters by their father. According to the terms of his will, the fortune was to be divided among twenty-nine charities after the death of his daughters, provided they left no heirs. None of this money, however, could be allotted to the Sisters of the Blessed Sacrament, since they had been founded after Mr. Drexel's will was made.

Those who were privileged to visit Mother Katharine during her confinement were imbued with the fragrance of her love for the Lord. It almost seemed as if she chose to spend her last days on her invalid's bed in order that her zealous daughters might mend any loose fences and be soundly established financially before she went home to heaven and they were deprived of her income. That income is estimated to have been $1,000 a day.

Priests who visited Mother Katharine during her last years say that they often saw her kissing the picture of the Sacred Heart, and that she smiled as she showed them a little card bearing the likeness of Pope Leo XIII. Sometimes it was as if she were whispering to her sainted friend, telling him not to be impatient, for her work was not yet finished.

Late in February 1955, a common cold weakened Mother Katharine, but there seemed to be no cause for alarm. A close friend, Father Louis Pastorelli, was in the habit of visiting her around the middle of March each year. During the time Mother Drexel was recovering from her cold, the sisters were surprised by Father Pastorelli's sudden appearance. He was not expected for another two weeks. The morning after his arrival, as the priest stood beside the little bed, which had become Mother Katharine's altar of sacrifice, it was obvious that she shared her sisters' surprise.

"You've come early," she observed.

"Yes," he answered, "something impelled me to come earlier this year."

On March 3, 1955, Mother Mary Katharine Drexel, in the ninety-seventh year of her life, serenely passed into eternity as her spiritual daughters and the community chaplain gathered around her in prayer.

A solemn Pontifical Requiem Mass was celebrated by Archbishop John F. O'Hara in the Cathedral of Saints Peter and Paul, Philadelphia. The cathedral was filled to overflowing with bishops, clergy, religious, and dignitaries from all professions and trades. Blacks and Indians from all over the United States journeyed to Philadelphia to pay their last respects to their benefactress. Mother Katharine's remains were returned to the Motherhouse at Cornwells Heights and interred in a crypt beneath the chapel.

At the time of her death, Mother Katharine, who had started out with a little band of thirteen, left five hundred Sisters of the Blessed Sacrament to carry on her work. Today her sisters minister to Native and African American peoples in forty-eight locations spread across the United States and Haiti.

The "richest nun in the world" had given the treasure of treasures—the knowledge of God—to America's forgotten people of color.

Mother Katharine had lived to see her work receive popular acclaim. The Alliance of Catholic Women presented her with an award for being "Philadelphia's Great Lady." The president of Haiti journeyed to the Motherhouse to personally bestow upon Mother Katharine the Honor of Merit Medal from his republic. But perhaps the most fitting tribute to the patriotic, "flag-waving" Kate Drexel, is one neither she herself nor the members of her community were aware of. She is pictured with a group of notable American sons and daughters of the Church under the arch that forms the main entrance to Saint Matthew's Cathedral in Washington, D.C.

Mother Katharine's daughters and the children who inherited from her the precious gift of faith, have always believed that they have gained a powerful friend in heaven. And the Church has shown her agreement.

Chapter 13

Beatification

The morning of November 20, 1988, dawned crisp and clear in Rome, Italy. The scattered showers of the previous day had been blown away by brisk winds. All roads leading to Vatican City were crowded with pilgrims making their way toward Saint Peter's Basilica to witness the Beatification of the Venerable Katharine Drexel.

The expectant crowd, pausing in Saint Peter's Square before climbing the slight hill leading to the resplendent basilica, was composed of people representing many nations and all walks of life. There were elderly priests and nuns, some of whom had known Mother Katharine, as they were apt to refer to her in conversation. Then there were the younger religious, many of them Sisters of the Blessed Sacrament, still carrying on the work Katharine Drexel began by providing schools and social services for the most neglected Americans—Native and Black. There were hundreds of men and women who had attended the schools Katharine Drexel had founded and staffed. There were also a sprinkling of her relatives and scores of people who had been inspired by the life of this Philadelphia heiress who had given not only her fortune but also her entire life to God.

One group of pilgrims that had attracted attention included Robert Gutherman, the young man whose cure had made the beatification ceremony possible.

Robert was fourteen years old when he developed an ear infection that would eventually render him deaf. As an altar boy at Saint Charles Borromeo Church, just across the highway from the Sisters of the Blessed Sacrament Motherhouse at Bensalem, Pennsylvania, Robert had served Mass at the Motherhouse chapel from time to time and was well known to a number of the sisters.

Although Robert's doctors prescribed medication to relieve his pain, it proved ineffective. Even three different antibiotics failed to overcome the serious infection. Mrs. Gutherman, no longer able to bear the sight of her son's suffering, turned to the Sisters of the Blessed Sacrament for help. She brought Robert to the convent and asked permission to take him to Mother Katharine's tomb. There, intercessory prayers for Robert's healing were offered by the Gutherman family and the sisters.

When the infection continued to advance and became dangerous, Dr. Myles G. Turtz, F.A.C.S., decided that surgery was necessary. The operation confirmed that the infection had caused severe damage. Not only had Robert's eardrum been irreparably damaged but two of the three bones that conduct vibrations to the inner ear were completely destroyed.

After the surgery, Mrs. Gutherman remained at the hospital with Robert. When he finally awoke, he asked his mother why she had called him. Mrs. Gutherman assured Robert that she had not called him—and then began wondering. How could he have heard her answer him when his good ear lay on a pillow? Immediately, Mrs. Gutherman sought out the doctor. Though Robert insisted that he could hear with the ear that had been operated on, the doctor declared it "impossible."

Two weeks after being released from the hospital, Robert went for a check up. As the doctor examined Robert's ear, he was utterly amazed to find that it had *reproduced anatomy*. Robert had a completely new eardrum. The results of an audiogram also proved that Robert could indeed hear from that ear. The doctor could only say that this had never happened before in medical history. He could offer "no" explanation.

After a great deal of investigation, the event was officially recognized as a miracle. Robert, his relatives, and friends formed one of the most grateful groups assembled at Saint Peter's on November 20, 1988.

Ripples of excitement ran through the crowd as television crews with equipment pushed their way through, eager to record the ceremony soon to begin. Paths opened up as cardinals, bishops, priests, and deacons made their way through the crowd carrying their colorful robes and black cassocks.

This surge of humanity was surprisingly quiet, moving through the huge doors of Saint Peter's and finding seats, with well trained and formally attired ushers making sure the process was orderly. Once seated, people looked up in awe at the age-old masterpieces on the ceiling above and the standing statues they had only read about until now.

The main altar was festive with harvest flowers of every hue. A veiled banner hung from a nearby balcony lending an air of anticipation.

As a swell of music echoed through the basilica, His Holiness Pope John Paul II and a procession of cardinals, archbishops, bishops, priests, deacons and acolytes marched down the aisle. It seemed fitting that John Cardinal Krol, retired Archbishop of Philadelphia, Pennsylvania, who had been tireless in his efforts to bring this cause to the Vatican's attention, Cardinal John O'Connor, Archbishop of New York, who grew up as a neighbor of Katharine Drexel in Philadelphia, and Father

John Vaugh, Minister General of the Franciscan Order, should be in this procession.

Pope John Paul II mounted the steps to the altar, with Archbishop Anthony Bevilacqua of Philadelphia, Bishop Donald Pelotte, coadjutor of Gallop, New Mexico, and Auxiliary Bishop Joseph Francis of Newark, New Jersey, while other members of the procession took their places.

A Navajo Indian, Marie Tso Allen, recited an intercessory prayer-poem in her native language. Sister M. Juliana Haynes, then President of the Sisters of the Blessed Sacrament and first Black to administer the congregation, proclaimed the first reading from the Book of Daniel. Dr. Norman Francis, President of Xavier University, founded by Katharine Drexel, participated by praying for God's people.

At the presentation of the gifts, one of the Sisters of the Blessed Sacrament presented the Holy Father with a gold chasuble adorned with hand painted crosses and woven for the Pope by an Osage Indian who had attended one of the Sisters of the Blessed Sacrament schools. An altar cloth designed by a African American religious, using the symbol of the acacia tree, a sign of messianic restoration, was presented by an African American couple from Texas who had just celebrated their golden wedding anniversary. A chalice and paten of pottery decorated with Sioux symbols and designs and painted in the colors of a brilliant sunset were also among the gifts.

At the consecration, heads were bowed in reverence and thanksgiving. After Pope John Paul distributed Holy Communion to those at the altar, dozens of priests carried the Eucharist to the faithful in the basilica.

A hush fell over the congregation as the Holy Father rose for his homily. He offered a warm welcome to those who had come from so far away for the happy occasion. Then, after he acknowledged the presence of Cardinal Krol, Archbishop Bevilacqua, and fellow bishops from the United States, Pope John Paul II proceeded cordially, and with unmistakable warmth, to greet the Sisters of the Blessed Sacrament, who had continued to carry on the work of their foundress.

The Holy Father referred to Katharine Drexel's life as one of exceptional apostolic service and paid tribute to her as a woman of lively faith "who stood courageously for the rights of the oppressed." He referred to the injustices, stemming from racial prejudice, experienced by those she served—the Native Americans and the Blacks—and stressed the importance of the way she strove to alleviate their deprivation by providing educational opportunities. He referred to Katharine Drexel's conviction that truth sets people free—that truth being found in Jesus Christ. Those who had known Mother Katharine were especially moved when the Holy Father referred to her efforts to ever strengthen her love for Jesus, whom she adored and received every day in the Holy Eucharist. He made a comparison of the manner in which she emulated the Savior who had gathered his disciples around him by her gathering around her the Sisters of the Blessed Sacrament to continue her work of evangelization. He urged all to listen to the voice of the Eucharistic King and, like Katharine Drexel, to bear witness to the truth.

When Pope John Paul II declared Katharine Drexel to be Blessed, the audience broke into applause. At that moment the banner hanging from a balcony was dramatically unveiled, revealing a life-size image of Katharine Drexel, dressed in the habit of the Sisters of the Blessed Sacrament, with an Indian child on one side and a Black child on the other. The figures were superimposed on a field of blue in the shape of the continental United States. For a few minutes, the elation of the audience was visible as well as audible; some were moved to tears.

As the ceremony ended and the Holy Father led the procession down the aisle of Saint Peter's, pilgrims reached out joyously to touch their spiritual leader. Then ushers led a small group of people—lay as well as religious, who had known Katharine Drexel during her active years or had enjoyed the fruits of her labor and legacy—through the crowd and into a small chamber. There a special audience, a *bacianiana,* was held and these fortunate pilgrims kissed the Pontiff's ring, often referred to as the Fisherman's Ring.

The crowd of pilgrims seemed reluctant to disband, and leaving the basilica, they gathered again in Saint Peter's Square to exchange reactions to the treasured beauty of the day.

The morning following the beatification, the pilgrims gathered at Saint Mary Major Basilica for a Mass of Thanksgiving. A *Mass for an American Saint,* composed by William Fisher, an alumnus of Xavier University, was sung by the Xavier University Choir. After the prelude, the call to worship began with the Prayer of the Four Directions, a Native American prayer for peace, reconciliation, and thanksgiving. Deacon Victor Bull Bear of South Dakota read the prayer. Mother Katharine's Indian children expressed their joy and thanksgiving with bells, drums, and song. The Eagle Dancers from the Phillip Riley family of Laguna Pueblo, New Mexico, performed the Communion thanksgiving dance around the altar. Archbishop Anthony Bevilacqua, in his homily, compared Katharine Drexel to Moses, for like Moses she had set God's people free.

At the end of this Mass of Thanksgiving, buses transported all of the pilgrims present to the Vatican where they had an audience with Pope John Paul II.

Most of the American pilgrims, who had come from twenty-three states, were pleased that Katharine Drexel's cause had progressed more quickly than usual. Many were of the opinion that much credit had to be given to the zealous, energetic attention and efforts of Cardinal Krol of Philadelphia. They also sensed that no labors had been spared by Katharine Drexel's daughters-in-religion, who had worked tirelessly to assemble the necessary documents after Archbishop Krol had officially opened the process on February 27, 1964, at the request of Mother M. Anselm, superior general of the order at that time.

Father Nicholas B. Ferrante, C.SS.R., was the original postulator in Rome with Father Francis Litz, C.SS.R., of Philadelphia as the vice-postulator of Mother Katharine's cause. Upon Father Ferrante's death, Father Paul Molinari, S.J., carried on the work, while Monsignor James McGrath succeeded the late Father Litz as vice-postulator. Father Peter Gumpel, S.J., of the Jesuit Curia in Rome served as the relator for the cause.

There were a number of official proceedings, which supervised the collection and examination of Mother Katharine's writings. Testimony had been taken from those who knew her. Proof had to be given that devotion had not gone beyond the bounds of one not yet canonized. In 1980, Pope John Paul II made the decision that Katharine Drexel had possessed a genuine reputation of holiness.

The revised rules for causes of the saints requires that the use of theological and canonical case for the existence of heroic holiness in a life be given an historical context. The volumes in which all material relating to the cause are contained is called the *posito*. This *posito* took many years to complete. The task of demonstrating Katharine Drexel's holiness from childhood until and during her final illness was important. This required the presentation of family background, how she came to discern her religious vocation, the development of her apostolic work, and the religious community she had founded. This also necessitated an explanation of issues of racial tension in the United States as it affected Native and Black Americans and how this, in turn, affected the Catholic Church's efforts at evangelizing these two ethnic groups during Katharine Drexel's early years.

The *posito,* containing three volumes, was presented to the Congregation of Sacred Causes of Saints in July 1986. Eight priest-consultors and one presiding officer were given the task of studying the volumes. After thorough study and discussion, the nine priests voted unanimously that heroic holiness was present in Katharine Drexel's life. On Monday, January 27, 1987, the Holy Father signed the decree and Mother Katharine officially became the Venerable Katharine Drexel.

Prayers then began for miracles. Through the publication sent out by the Sisters of the Blessed Sacrament, anyone who received a favor that they felt was the result of the intercession of the Venerable Katharine Drexel was asked to forward such information to the Motherhouse in Bensalem, Pennsylvania, so that it might be sent on to Rome.

A board of physicians examined the cure of one, Robert Gutherman. After the physical examination of the young man's previously infected ear indicated that the cure was medically unexplainable, this information was added to the official documentation. Upon examination of all the official documents, the Congregation of Sacred Causes recommended that this cure be attributed to the intercession of Katharine Drexel. This was the one miracle needed for beatification. On July 22, 1988, Archbishop Anthony Bevilacqua announced that Pope John Paul II had given his approval and Katharine Drexel would be beatified.

As previously stated, much attention was centered on Robert Gutherman and his relatives during the activities connected to the beatification. However, Robert, the fourth of George and Beatrice Gutherman's eleven children, reminded all those present that this was *Mother Katharine's* cure. One of his brothers was quoted as saying that Robert provided an infected ear and Mother Katharine did the rest! Robert was twenty-eight years old at the time of the beatification. Today he is married and is the father of two children.

Chapter 14

The Second Miracle

One more miracle was necessary before Blessed Katharine Drexel could be canonized. Mysteriously, it would again come to a Philadelphia-area child suffering from deafness.

Amanda—affectionately known as Amy—the third child of Constance and John Wall, was born in 1992 with nerve deafness in both ears. Mrs. Wall was the first to recognize that her baby daughter couldn't hear. In September 1993, a series of medical tests confirmed that Amy's auditory nerve deafness was congenital and irreversible.

In November 1993, the Wall family watched a PBS documentary on Blessed Katharine Drexel and learned of Robert Gutherman's miraculous healing. The Walls began begging Blessed Katharine to obtain for them the grace to simply communicate with Amy.

In January, the two-year-old started making signs to indicate when she wanted milk or a cookie. Mrs. Wall felt that their prayers had been answered. But this progress wasn't enough for her seven-year-old son Jack, a firm believer in miracles. "I'm going to pray for a cure," he informed his mother at the end of February. "And I'm going to pray that if Amy can't be cured, I will be deaf too so we can be the same," Jeanette, Amy's six-year-old sister broke in.

The Walls went ahead with faith and solicited the prayers of family members and friends. One friend brought them a medal of Blessed Katharine. Another dropped off a holy card containing her relic. The parents placed the medal on Amy's crib and touched the relic to her ears as the family continued to storm heaven.

Sometime around March 3 (the feast day of Blessed Katharine), Amy's preschool teacher made an amazing discovery—Amy was beginning to respond to sounds. Mr. and Mrs. Wall reacted cautiously at first, but they did arrange for more medical tests. The results? Amy's hearing was now inexplicably normal!

The Walls excitedly wrote to the Sisters of the Blessed Sacrament. The sisters, in turn, informed Cardinal Anthony Bevilacqua. On Friday, December 20, 1996, an official archdiocesan inquiry into the case was opened.

Numerous physicians, including ear, nose, and throat specialists and audiologists meticulously pored over Amy's medical records. The group of doctors was composed of those who had previously treated Amy and independent experts called in by the Philadelphia archdiocese and the Vatican. The archdiocesan medical team was made up of Jewish, Moslem, Hindu, and Catholic doctors. All the doctors on this medical team agreed that there was no scientific, natural, or medical explanation for Amy's cure.

On January 5, 2000, the board of theologians appointed to study the case judged that Amy Wall's healing was due to the intercession of Blessed Katharine Drexel. On January 27, Pope John Paul II publicly recognized Amy's healing as a miracle attributed to Blessed Katharine.

Mother Katharine Drexel was solemnly canonized at Saint Peter's Basilica in Rome on October 1, 2000. She is only the second native-born United States citizen to be so honored.

The author of this book received her high school diploma from the hands of Mother Katharine Drexel on June 6, 1923, when she graduated from Saint Francis de Sales, Rock Castle, Virginia, one of the many schools Mother Katharine had established for America's neglected. As these lines were first written, a prayer was whispered that one day it could be said that this old, tattered diploma was touched by *Saint* Katharine Drexel.

This dream has now come true.

Saint Katharine Drexel, pray for us!

Prayers and Contemplative Reflections from the Personal Writings of Saint Katharine Drexel

To the Holy Spirit

O most holy and adorable Spirit of my Jesus, let me hear your sweet voice. O Divine Spirit I wish to be before you as a light feather, so that your breath may carry me where you will.

O Holy Spirit, O Eternal Deity, Christ-Love, come into my heart. By your power attract it to you, my God, and grant me charity. Preserve me, O ineffable Love, from all evil thoughts. Inflame me with your love in order that all my sufferings be light to me, my Holy Father and gracious Lord. Finally, assist me in all my ministry. Christ-Love! Christ-Love! Amen.

Eucharistic Adoration

I thank you, O my Jesus, through Mary, for having loved me and delivered yourself for me, for us. O how strong and powerful, how generous and noble is your love.

Grant us, O loving Mother, a share in your sentiments, that like you, we may from now on know how to console, to make reparation, and to be compassionate.

O Jesus, I adore you in the Host of exposition. This act of adoration is no trivial act, but will certainly sanctify and transform my soul. I adore your heart, which desires me to unite myself to your sufferings.

O memorial of the wonders of God's love! Take our cold hearts prisoner, draw them to yourself, for a heart is not worthy to beat that does not beat for you alone!

O Mary, our Mother, who will excuse us for our negligence and lukewarmness toward this wondrous Sacrament of the Eucharist! Intercede for us now, convert us, inflame us that at last we may begin to return your divine Son love for love! Amen.

Ah, Lord, it is but too true, YOU ARE NOT LOVED! Shall we not strive by every means in our power to make you known and loved? Shall we not try to pay many an extra visit to our dearest Friend, ever present in the Blessed Sacrament, ever living to make intercession for us? And may this prayer, dearest Lord, be on our lips when we bow down in lowly adoration in your sacramental presence: "O Sacred Heart of Jesus, you love! O Sacred Heart of Jesus, you are not loved! O would that you were loved!" Our Lady, open your heart to me, your child. Teach me to know your Son intimately, to love him ardently, and to follow him closely.

The Eucharist is a never-ending sacrifice. It is the Sacrament of love, the act of love. Help me each moment today and always to communicate myself to you by doing your will. Let the doing of your will each moment be a spiritual communion. In it you will give me yourself; I will give you myself.

To Mary

O Mary, make me endeavor, by all the means in my power, to extend the kingdom of your Divine Son and offer incessantly my prayers for the conversion of those who are yet in darkness or estranged from his fold.

O holy Mother of God, behold your child! I am not worthy, but Jesus gave me to you. I am a part of his legacy; teach me to be all that a child of Mary ought to be.

Holy Mary, stand by me in all the actions of my life and do not abandon me at the hour of death!

Teach me, O my dear Mother, as I kneel with you at the foot of the cross—teach me the lesson of sacrifice. Let me learn it here at the feet of Jesus crucified. O my Mother, let me never forget that many sins have been forgiven me. May I, like Magdalene, be faithful to the end, standing firm and clinging to Jesus in spite of repugnancies, interior rebellions, darkness, and temptation. Help me, my Mother, to take from the hands of Jesus in the spirit of humble love, my daily crosses—the weariness and disappointments of life and all that it costs to struggle against self, to sacrifice self for our Lord's glory. Help me, Mother, to console the Sacred Heart of Jesus by being a messenger of his love.

For Courage

Dear Jesus, my Lord and my God, give me courage, fortitude and loyalty in your service. Grant me sincerity, earnestness, patience, humility, and above all holy love. My God, I love you!

Help me to conform my will totally to yours, to say with all my heart, "Not my will but yours be done." In your Sacred Heart, let me find strength and courage to suffer with and for you. O sweet Jesus, my love and my only good! I beg and implore you to give me the grace never to seek rest or satisfaction away from you. O Virgin Mother of God, my Mother, pray to Jesus for me.

For Confidence

Grant me, O Lord, for the sake of your glory, the special gift of confidence, which is above all virtue and the most gracious gift you can bestow upon your devoted friends. Lord, establish me most firmly in the state of confidence, which is the most glorious for you and the most profitable for the Church.

I do not want to stand on my own legs and walk where my selfish will urges me to go. I long for the loving trust of a child, nesting confidently on your warm bosom. I beg you, Divine Spouse of my soul, through Mary, to taste how sweet, you, O Lord are. I beg that I may so long for you that my prayer may become incessant and my yearning for your presence uninterrupted.

For Love and Self-Surrender

O, give me, dear Mother Mary and Joseph, your love for Jesus, the depth of its tenderness. Grant me the grace of surrendering myself in all that shall happen to me today and in the future, to the mercy of God. God is all and at his summons everything must give way, even joy and happiness, which counts for nothing when he calls. If he calls to sorrow, he knows what is best, since faith and love feel real happiness by following where he leads.

As bread is changed into Jesus Christ, so must I be changed into Jesus Christ so that he will live in me alone. I pray and I beg through Mary and Joseph for utter detachment from all that I must leave in death.

Yes, my Lord and my God Jesus, to you I commend my spirit, my soul with its faculties, my body with its senses, my heart with its affections, all that I have, and all that I am. Dispose of me absolutely, in everything, according to your will. From now on, dearest Jesus, may everything outside you be a matter of indifference to me, provided only I accomplish your will and advance in your love. O Jesus, I love you and your Mother and abandon myself to your love for time and eternity.

Passion Prayer

O my dear Jesus, through your sacred wounds and agonizing death, grant me the grace to expire in your love and friendship. O Sacred Heart of Jesus, I believe in your love for me. O Jesus, Divine Savior grant that I no longer be deaf to your heavenly call but prompt and diligent in accomplishing your will. Make me yours at any cost. Give me courage to overcome every obstacle in your holy service. Draw me continually, dearest Jesus, to closer union with you.

Prayer for Union with God

I hope and desire through Mary that my heart shall ever practically be united to the Lord. Uphold me, Lord, and I shall live. Let me never be separated from you. My place is in God, in his justice, in his love. May no sin ever separate me from him. Far away in the desert of sin, you sought this straying sheep so often. It would be fitting I should bathe your feet with my tears! You make my soul plunge into incomparable love—the love which I hope for of your forgiveness in confession.

Let us be followers of God and walk in love, as Christ also has loved us and has delivered himself for us.

Love does not consist of great sweetness of devotion, but in a most fervent determination to strive to please God in all things.

So now in the sacrament of Eucharistic love he still abides in littleness to stay with us always.

The act of loving God is eternal.

Love is proved by deeds.

Our Lord likes courage. Get it from him. You won't find it in yourself.

I have discovered how to pray in an extremely efficacious manner. The Heart of Jesus is also my heart, since I am a member of his body. And with this Heart I will pray to God, my Father, and my prayer will always be heard.

In failure! Good Jesus, supply what is wanting. I offer his Heart in atonement and ask help.

How I would miss our Lord if he were to be away from me by his presence in the Blessed Sacrament! O joy, today I shall see him lifted up in the white consecrated Host and in his Precious Blood in the chalice. Would that I could meet him truly as his handmaid, his pleasure, in my soul. Make me faithful to him even as Mary was faithful to him at Bethlehem and on the Hill of Skulls. I am needy and poor and I seek the strength to do this.

My sweetest joy is to be in the presence of Jesus in the holy Sacrament. I beg that when obliged to withdraw in body, I may leave my heart before the Blessed Sacrament. When after benediction the priest locks the sacred Host in the tabernacle, I beg Jesus to lock me in the tabernacle until morning.

I desire God alone and to forget myself entirely, and I abandon myself to God that he may do with me absolutely whatever he may will.

Love! Love! Let us give ourselves to real, pure Love! Devotion to the Sacred Heart is the devotion, which alone can banish the coldness of our times. The renewal which I (we) seek is a work of love and can be accomplished by love alone.

Think over the words of our Blessed Mother's *Magnificat*. Let us say: I will take hold of the hand of my Mother whom God in his goodness and mercy and love gave to me. I will look up into her loving countenance and meet the encouraging gaze of her, the sinless one, looking upon one who is not sinless, yet seeing in me one who has been made by baptism (through God's love and mercy) a child of God. We can address her. "O sweet Spouse of the Holy Spirit...." We can imagine her saying sentence by sentence the *Magnificat*—then listening as we repeat back to her, "My soul magnifies the Lord!"

We ask that we who have the love of God in our hearts, who possess, that is, sanctifying grace, may keep it unto the end and thereby merit to be presented by Mary, our Mother, in God's holy temple where all grace will become glory. All comes to us through Mary. As she brought her Son into the temple at Jerusalem, so she brings him into the temple of our hearts and finally will bring us into the temple of God's glory.

When you are suffering, reflect that Jesus is bestowing on you some small portion of his cross. Be not discouraged.

He may be leading me out to a cross. If so, I can have no hesitation about following him. He has given me many proofs of his goodness and his love. I know his voice so well. Who else would call me so distinctly by my name! I must follow, I must follow him closely, so that when the cross is reached I shall be near him, my Good Shepherd, who will help me to carry it, for he still bears his cross in each one of his children—"He carries our sorrows."

I trust him, love him, have faith in his power.

About the Author

Ellen Tarry's multifaceted career began a half century ago when she taught in the public schools of her native Birmingham, Alabama, following upon graduation from Alabama State College. As a teacher of Black children during those dark years in the South, she realized how important it was for students to understand their history and the emerging world. She became a journalist and her first weekly column was "Negroes of Note."

Ellen moved to New York City and began working for social justice with Father Michael F. Mulvoy, C.S.Sp. in Saint Mark the Evangelist Parish located in the heart of Harlem. She subsequently worked with the late Baroness Catherine de Hueck at Harlem's Friendship House. At the invitation of Bishop Bernard J. Sheil, Ellen went to Chicago to assist in setting up a Friendship House in the predominantly Black South Side of the city.

She later returned to New York City to work as a feature writer at *The New York Amsterdam News* and contributed to leading Catholic publications. When the clouds of World War II darkened, she was drafted to work with the national Catholic Community Service-U.S.O. Clubs throughout the country.

Because of her interest in writing, Ellen became a member of the first Writer's Laboratory at Bank Street College, New York City.

She joined the New York Regional Office of the Department of Housing and Urban Development as a relocations advisor, and then as an equal opportunity officer. When she retired from HUD, the late Terence Cardinal Cooke bestowed a medal on her in recognition of her work in the service of the Church. She later received the *Pro Ecclesia Et Pontifice* Medal from His Holiness, Pope John Paul II.

Ellen is a member of the New York Coalition of 100 Black Women, the New York Chapter of the National Association of Media Women, the Schomburg Corporation, Commissioner Emeritus of the Office of Black Ministry, Archdiocese of New York, and has served as a non-governmental observer at the United Nations.

She is the mother of one daughter, Elizabeth Tarry Patton, a former teacher in the New York City Schools.

BOOKS & MEDIA

*The Daughters of St. Paul operate book and media centers at
the following addresses. Visit, call or write the one nearest you
today, or find us on the World Wide Web, www.pauline.org*

CALIFORNIA
    3908 Sepulveda Blvd., Culver City, CA 90230; 310-397-8676
    5945 Balboa Ave., San Diego, CA 92111; 858-565-9181
    46 Geary Street, San Francisco, CA 94108; 415-781-5180
FLORIDA
    145 S.W. 107th Ave., Miami, FL 33174; 305-559-6715
HAWAII
    1143 Bishop Street, Honolulu, HI 96813; 808-521-2731
    Neighbor Islands call: 800-259-8463
ILLINOIS
    172 North Michigan Ave., Chicago, IL 60601; 312-346-4228
LOUISIANA
    4403 Veterans Memorial Blvd., Metairie, LA 70006; 504-887-7631
MASSACHUSETTS
    Rte. 1, 885 Providence Hwy., Dedham, MA 02026; 781-326-5385
MISSOURI
    9804 Watson Rd., St. Louis, MO 63126; 314-965-3512
NEW JERSEY
    561 U.S. Route 1, Wick Plaza, Edison, NJ 08817; 732-572-1200
NEW YORK
    150 East 52nd Street, New York, NY 10022; 212-754-1110
    78 Fort Place, Staten Island, NY 10301; 718-447-5071
OHIO
    2105 Ontario Street, Cleveland, OH 44115; 216-621-9427
PENNSYLVANIA
    9171-A Roosevelt Blvd., Philadelphia, PA 19114; 215-676-9494
SOUTH CAROLINA
    243 King Street, Charleston, SC 29401; 843-577-0175
TENNESSEE
    4811 Poplar Ave., Memphis, TN 38117; 901-761-2987
TEXAS
    114 Main Plaza, San Antonio, TX 78205; 210-224-8101
VIRGINIA
    1025 King Street, Alexandria, VA 22314; 703-549-3806
CANADA
    3022 Dufferin Street, Toronto, Ontario, Canada M6B 3T5; 416-781-9131
    1155 Yonge Street, Toronto, Ontario, Canada M4T 1W2; 416-934-3440

¡También somos su fuente para libros, videos y música en español!